THE BIG BIG BIG BRISTOW BOOK

by

Frank Dickens

C000203565

I CAN'T UNDERSTAND
SIR REGINALD CHESTER-PERRY...
I KNOW HE HAS HIS
NAME WRITTEN RIGHT ACROSS
THE FRONT OF THE BUILDING
BUT IT'S TOO LOW **DOWN**....
HE OUGHT TO HAVE IT
WRITTEN ALONG THE TOP OF
THE BUILDING— WHERE IT
CAN BE SEEN FROM MILES
AWAY....

THE R.L.CHESTER -PERRY COMPANY...

P.S. IF YOU CAN READ THIS
YOU ARE TOO CLOSE...

L. CHESTER- PERRY CO. LTD.

A Little, Brown Book

First published in Great Britain in 2001
by Litte, Brown and Company

Copyright © 2001 Frank Dickens

The moral right of the author has been asserted.

All rights reserved.
No part of this publication may be reproduced, stored in a
retrieval system, or transmitted, in any form or by any means, without
the prior permission in writing of the publisher, nor be otherwise
circulated in any form of binding or cover other than that in which
it is published and without a similar condition including this
condition being imposed on the subsequent purchaser.

A CIP catalogue record for this book
is available from the British Library

ISBN 0 316 85822 6

Typeset by M Rules
Printed and bound in Great Britain
by Butler & Tanner

Little, Brown and Company (UK)
Brettenham House
Lancaster Place
London WC2E 7EN

THE BIG BIG BIG BRISTOW BOOK

LITTLE, BROWN AND COMPANY

AUTHOR'S NOTE.

When the first Bristow compilation was published, my sister Pamela complained that after reading a third of it she was forced to hurl the book against the wall. When asked why, she replied that up until that point, Bristow had not actually **done** any work at all, and the sheer frustration had driven her to make this critical protest.

I took note and, when the second compilation hit the bookstalls, ensured that Bristow was immediately committed to Getting On With It.

Another complaint from the same source. This time it was her breathing. The book made her breathless. Upon being cross-examined she explained that there were so many gags crammed together that the brain could not recover in time to fully appreciate each individual punchline and ran into oxygen debt. The book needed 'timing'.

I once again took note and when this volume was being put together, took care to leave plenty of gulping time. A repetition of cartoon strips does induce a gentle hammering on the brain that develops into a relentless pounding not unlike that of Chinese water torture. Heavy poundings not being the best thing to hand out if one wishes to earn a crust, I have decided to break up the strips with some gentle ramblings, in no particular order and of no particular importance.

I hope Pamela does not find the mixture too heady.

There are those readers, I am sure, who prefer to see compilations of strip cartoons in their original state, dog eared and blotchy, with corrections and additions added to or deleted by layers of corrective fluid or gummed on pieces of paper, but I am not one of these. There will also, I suspect, be much gnashing of teeth by those same readers at the lack of original artwork, usually provided by authors more sensitive than myself, in order to trace the artistic development of the strip, but you'll get no apology from me. True, there are a few, left in to illustrate a valid historical point, but most of the book has been redrawn. Vintage, is what I like. And vintage is what you get.

INTRODUCTION.

Bristow, a daily comic strip that appeared in the **Evening Standard** for almost forty years and was discarded by huntin' shootin' fishin' editor, Max Hastings, who decided 'the age of the bowler hat is over', is the name of a Buying Clerk of no certain age who works for the monolithic Chester-Perry Organisation. At the time it was dropped I had written and drawn over ten thousand strips; remarkable when it was originally conceived as an instruction on motor car maintenance, and only thirteen strips out of the ten thousand had featured both man and vehicle.

The vehicle was an Austin 7 Chummy, rebuilt by Colin Chapman of Lotus fame (who went to the same school as yours truly) and, in the curiously naïve way that lads of my age had then, I hoped to explain – by way of a strip cartoon – the intricacies of the combustion engine and the maintenance and upkeep of a motor car.

Here is a photograph of my good self and the car in question, taken forty years ago.

Below is the first strip. (A few weeks before it started I had seen a cartoon drawn by Michael Ffolkes, in which the name Bristow *was featured, and being a rather nondescript name I attached it to the insignificant driver).* Bristow *is seen driving the car to the office.*

My plan was to show the car. The following day the Bristow *character was to be driving home and experience a breakdown.*

He was to explain that the trouble was due to a broken half shaft and he was having to repair it IN HIS OWN TIME. *Explaining away a broken half shaft in the limited space of a cartoon frame proved rather more difficult than I anticipated, and while I tried to work out how to present this successfully, decided to delay the action and keep him in the office until the solution presented itself.*

And in the office, apart from an occasional foray into the world outside, in search of food, or the occasional holiday, he has remained.

EIGHT HOURS TO GO—
EIGHT HOURS!!
JUST THINK OF IT...
EIGHT MORE **HOURS**...
THAT'S FOUR HUNDRED
AND EIGHTY MINUTES!
FOUR HUNDRED AND
EIGHTY TIMES SIXTY
IS........
TWENTY EIGHT
THOUSAND, EIGHT
HUNDRED...!!!!
THERE ARE
TWENTY EIGHT
THOUSAND, EIGHT
HUNDRED **SECONDS**
TO GO!!!

ONE....TWO....THREE...FOUR.....

1. ONCE UPON A TIME.

Bristow was, before he became a leading character in the strip, a rather shadowy figure. I lifted him from a story of mine called 'Good Grief' which appeared in a book entitled **What the Dickens**.

The story concerned a man who was trying to kill his wife. (I was undergoing some kind of crisis at the time and the whole book consisted of stories about men trying to rid themselves of their wives by causing mayhem at home.) But he he had a smile that somehow stayed with me . . .

"DOCTOR – HOW DO YOU DIE OF A BROKEN HEART?"
THE DOCTOR THOUGHT A BIT...
"YOU GRIEVE" HE SAID...
"YOU GRIEVE AND GRIEVE AND GRIEVE UNTIL YOU DIE"...
THEN HE LOOKED UP...
"THANKS DOC" HE WHISPERED...
AND HE WHISTLED ALL THE WAY HOME...

THE FIRST THING HE DID WAS RELEASE HER BUDGERIGAR...

"THE BUDGIE'S GONE DEAR" HE CALLED...

SHE RAN INTO THE GARDEN, HER FACE WHITE...

"YOU LOOK PALE, DEAR" HE MURMURED.

"IT'S FLOUR" SHE EXPLAINED, "I'M MAKING PASTRY FOR SUPPER."

SMOTHERING A CURSE HE WENT INTO THE GARDEN AND PULLED UP HER FAVOURITE FLOWERS...

"VANDALS HAVE BROKEN IN AND DESTROYED THE BLOOMS!" HE SAID.

SHE CAME OUT FROM THE KITCHEN WITH TEARS IN HER EYES. "DARLING, YOU ARE CRYING" HE SAID....

"I'VE BEEN PEELING ONIONS" SHE LAUGHED..

"BUT YOU CAN HARDLY SPEAK."..

"M-M-M-MOUTHFUL OF H-H-H-HOT PASTRY" SHE REPLIED...

"IT'S NO USE" HE MUTTERED, "I'LL NEVER GET RID OF HER..."

Having placed this character in an office, I decided to keep him there while I worked on the car angle. It was the least I could do. The car was the star, after all. I loved that car and was determined that the World would share my devotion.

Colin Chapman, old schoolfriend, had turned his Austin 7 Chummy into a successful racing machine and, well meaning though they undoubtedly were, the makers of the Chummy had not designed it to burble around breaking records or they would have incorporated heavier and sturdier half shafts.

Colin was ahead of the game. He disposed of the car that was devouring half shafts like a panda going through bamboo shoots and began to build his own: Lotus racing cars.

And he disposed of the Chummy in my direction.

What does one do when one finds one's self in possession of a get-up-and-go motor car at loggerheads with its rather naff half shafts? Answer: One tires of aforementioned vehicle. That, dear reader, is exactly what happened to me. I tired of motor cars. There was nothing amusing in motor cars. I began to dislike motor cars. I HATED motor cars.

And I began to think more about the man I had left stranded in the office.

WHAT A LIFE!

AS WE LEFT THE OFFICE ON FRIDAY IT STARTED TO RAIN.....
IT POURED RIGHT THROUGH THE WEEKEND AND ALL THE WAY HERE THIS MORNING....
THEN, AS WE ENTERED THE **CHESTER-PERRY** BUILDING THE RAIN STOPPED AND OUT IT CAME.....

NINE TILL FIVE SUNSHINE!

2. THE PLOT THICKENS.

Even in these days of High Security one can, if one had a sufficiently imposing piece of paper, stroll around corridors, or even sit down for a while at a desk, in a large organisation, without being asked for identification. But one is pushing one's luck to do this on a regular basis.

In order to give Bristow credibility while I waited for the broken half shaft situation to sort itself out I therefore had to give him a job.

I needed something nondescript. And the most nondescript office job, in those far off thirty six years ago days, was a buying clerk. Post boy was the lowest, Buying Clerk next. Post Boy, Buying Clerk, was the pecking order. I decided to give Bristow a job in the Buying Department and, to give him a target at which to aim, made him eighteenth in line for Chief Buyer. What seemed to be a good idea at the time, made it neccessary to expand the size of the firm to a staff of at least nineteen, and to house that number, a much larger premises was required. Much larger . . .

THERE IT IS....
THE **CHESTER-PERRY** BUILDING.....

A MIRACLE OF MODERN CONSTRUCTION....
IT TOOK AN ARMY OF WORKMEN TWO YEARS TO BUILD THAT PLACE....
JUST GIVE ME A

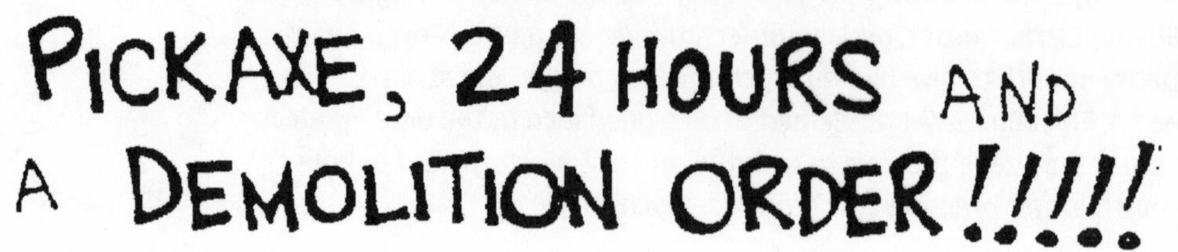
PICKAXE, 24 HOURS AND
A DEMOLITION ORDER!!!!!

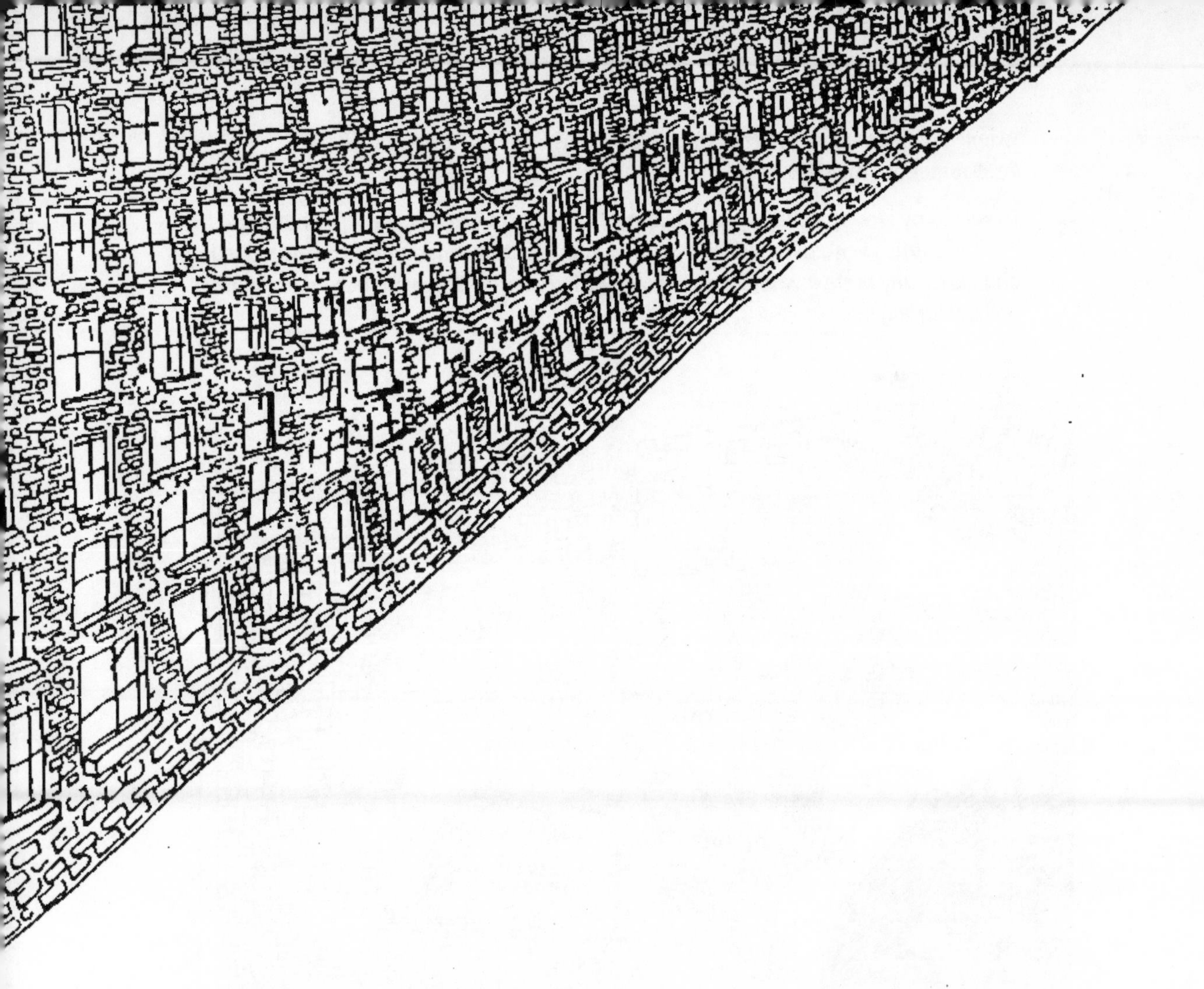

3. A BIG DOLL'S HOUSE.

The Chester-Perry building is a marriage of two structures that were part of my growing up. The first was Brittain's pickle factory in Tottenham Lane, London N8, and the second a modern monstrosity in Muswell Hill.

I was born next door to the pickle factory and spent the early and formative years of my life playing in the alley that ran down one side of the monstrous Victorian edifice. It was, however, long and low (this was before high-rise), so when I began to shop around for a suitable modern office for Bristow I decided to place him in a building that was a combination of the two. Having joined them up, I simply moved them to the City.

Twinned with the Devil's Island, the building was to play a large part in the development of the strip.

Thwarted by lack of technical knowledge and unable to draw half shafts that looked like half shafts I vented my spleen by drawing bricks and windows. At the drop of a hat and under any pretext whatsoever I would pick up a pen and get cracking on another architectural gem.

I was beginning to like drawing the place. After all, I knew something of the architecture . . .

and something about the people who worked there . . .

JUST LISTEN TO THAT COURIER RABBITING ON....
A WORD OR TWO MORE ABOUT THIS IMPRESSIVE BUILDING
IMPRESSIVE BUILDING, MY FOOT.... IF I HAD MY WAY I'D BLOW THE PLACE SKY HIGH....
ON THIS SITE THERE ORIGINALLY STOOD AN OLD PRISON, WHERE MISCREANTS WERE INCARCERATED FOR MANY LONG YEARS....
RUMOUR HAS IT THAT HERE WAS AN ENTRANCE KNOWN AS TRAITOR'S GATE....
EXCUSE ME... EXCUSE ME..

HELLO — THAT CROWD OF TOURISTS ARE GETTING READY TO MOVE OFF...
GOOD RIDDANCE, TOO — GAWKING AT US LIKE THAT....
WHAT DO THEY THINK WE ARE — ANIMALS IN SOME KIND OF ZOO..?
THEY'RE OFF — HOLY MACKEREL!!
WE HAVE SEEN THE WORKERS AT CHESTER-PERRYS

I HATE THE PLACE!
IT TAKES FIVE MINUTES TO GET OUT........
AND TEN MINUTES TO GET CLEAR!

At the odd social gathering . . .

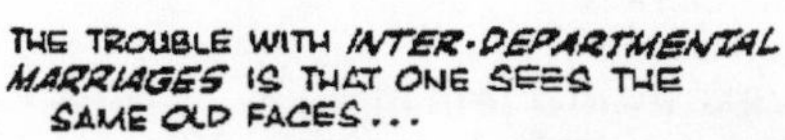

But when I saw Bristow drawing it, I decided to give it a rest for a while.

4. PROFILE.

Suffice to say then, so far we have Bristow, eighteenth in line for Chief Buyer, working for the monolithic Chester-Perry Company in the Chester-Perry building.

The next question that had to be asked is: 'What does a Buying Clerk do?'

This should have been easy, for I was once employed in that capacity in a firm in Tottenham. To explain why it is not easy, I will reveal a little of my own background.

In the days before drawing a cartoon about motor cars became an obsession, I had been passionately interested in bicycle racing. To succeed in the sport I had joined the firm because I had been reliably informed that they possessed a sports ground with FACILITIES. This was the equivalent of a bugle call to a young warhorse. I was pounding on the door and demanding a job. Any job. The job I was offered – and took on the spot – was the job of a buying clerk (one above Post Boy, remember). No matter. I was employed by a firm that boasted a sports ground AND facilities.

I had been since birth a stoic child. No emoting from this kiddo. No squeals of delight when I ran into the playground at going home time. The football that the Mayor of Hornsey pressed into my hands for being the Best Boy at St Mary's Mixed Infants was received with the same indifference I expressed when five minutes later he took it back and presented it to another lad saying he had made a mistake.

But this self control exploded into fury on my second day at Keith Blackman Ltd. when I discovered I had joined the wrong firm. They did not possess either a sports ground OR the facilities. I had joined the wrong lot. I SHOULD have joined Standard Telephones and Cables at Southgate.

The fury that I felt upon learning of this mega blunder did not manifest itself in breaking windows of shredding documents, but rather the reverse. I withdrew into my shell, ignoring my surroundings and fellow workers, and never found out what business they were in until many years later, when I was working for Standard Telephones and Cables, and using **their** Sports ground and Facilities.

I spent the remaining days of my time at Keith Blackman's looking out of the window and, I am ashamed to say, learning nothing.

(This last is not strictly true. I passed a couple of hours writing a children's story which was published many years later, under the title **Fly Away, Peter** *with pictures by Ralph Steadman. One of the reasons Ralph did the illustrations was that the story was about a bird and I could not draw birds. My attempts later materialised in the strip.)*

5. THE ESTABLISHMENT.

It is now time to speak of the Establishment. The Hierarchy, and when I say that, I am referring to Sir Reginald Chester-Perry, the firm's founder. We know he EXISTS. He has been seen . . .

and we know that Jones, having undergone a stringent cross examination, knows his stuff . . .

But with others we are not too sure . . .

Sir Reginald represents many things to many people.

To some, a meal ticket . . .

To others, a mere statistic . . .

But to the likes of Bristow and lesser mortals he will probably be just another face in the back-seat in the Rolls Royce of life.

I once met a man who claimed to be Sir Reginald.

It was in Sardinia and I was staying with some Italian friends. Among these was one chap who was not really **of the crowd**. *Like the Flying Dutchman, he was always to be found on the fringes, hovering, so to speak, and although omnipresent, never made himself known. On the day in question I found myself lumbered with him. The rest of the gang were elsewhere and we were stuck with each other. I speak no Italian and, lost for something to say, I turned to him and shrugged.*

He smiled. 'I speak English,' he said reassuringly.

'I didn't realise that,' I replied.

'I know,' he grinned. 'You never speak to me.'

'Sorry,' I said. 'You are—?'

'Sir Reginald Chester-Perry,' he smiled.

I thought he was speaking Italian.

'Sorry,' I said. 'I don't speak Italian.'

'I am not speaking Italian,' he laughed. 'Sir Reginald Chester-Perry.' He began to speak slowly. 'I am Sir Reginald Chester-Perry. Your character.'

'Really,' I replied, putting him down as a head-case, and moved away to finish carving a cribbage board I had started earlier.

He turned out to be Pirelli of Pirelli Tyres.

From thereon yours truly could always be found hovering on the fringes of the crowd.

6. ON YOUR KNEES!

Frederick J. Fudge, Chief Buyer for the company, is Bristow's immediate superior.

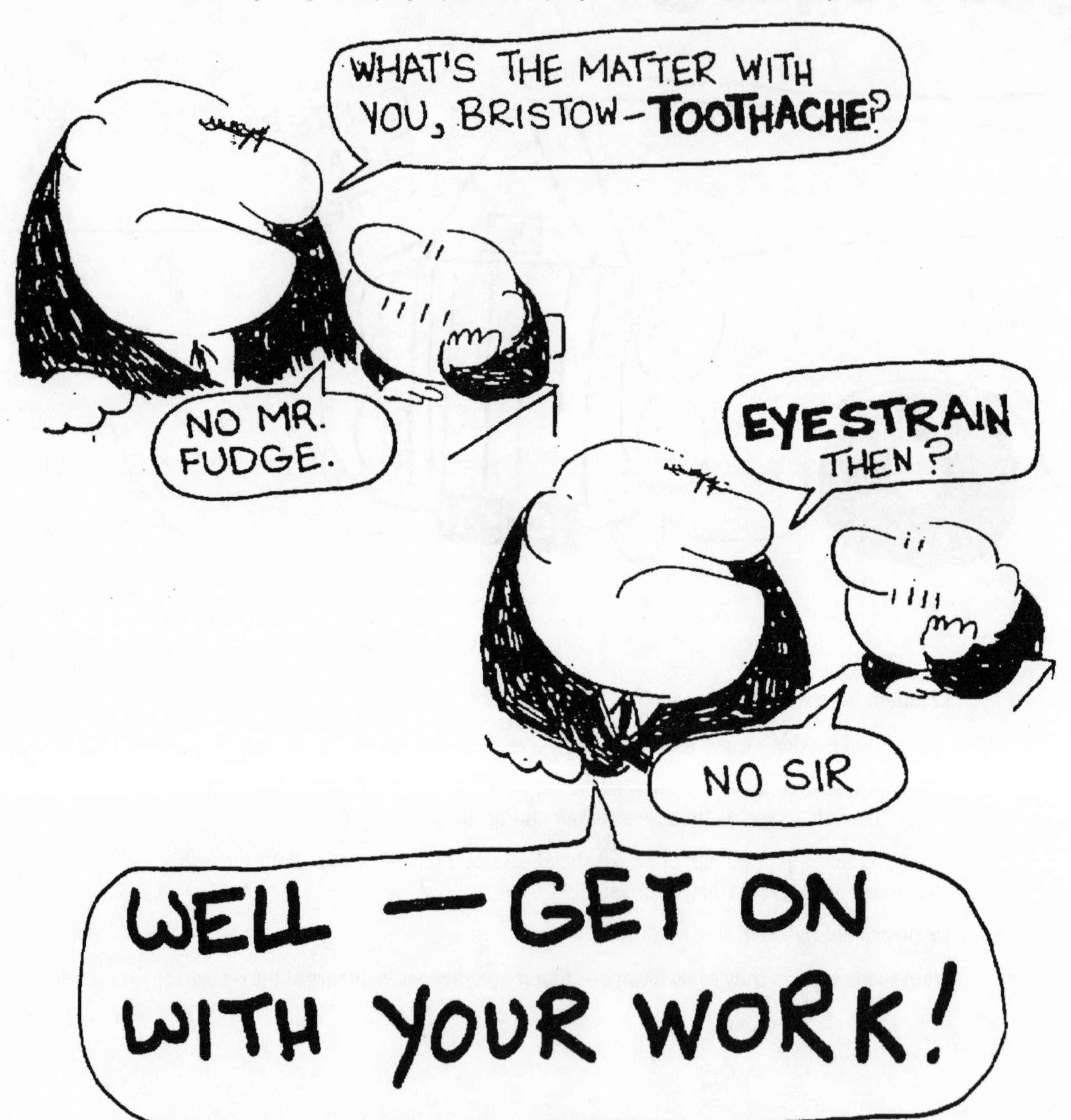

TOOTHACHE AND EYESTRAIN INDEED! THE MAN'S A FOOL!
I'VE BEEN GIVING HIM THE SAME LOOK FOR NEARLY EIGHT YEARS....
HE STILL DOESN'T RECOGNISE DUMB INSOLENCE!!

Since Bristow's definition of the perfect Chief Buyer is someone who 'knocks on his door before he comes out', Fudge comes as a cruel disappointment. He is a tyrant, his role in the strip extolling Bristow to 'GET ON WITH IT!'

We know very little about this man, and I think we ought to leave it this way.

THAT FUDGE IS A PIG....
HE JUST PASSED ME IN THE STREET AND DIDN'T SAY A WORD...
I TROT OUT THE OLD 'GOOD MORNING, MR. FUDGE' AND HE IGNORES ME COMPLETELY!
IF I HADN'T BEEN FORAGING THROUGH A DUSTBIN AT THE TIME I'D HAVE RUN AFTER HIM AND GIVEN HIM A PIECE OF MY MIND.........

7. STRAIGHT MAN.

If we are going by the number of appearances in the strip I suppose JONES must claim second prize. He was mentioned in a very early episode . . .

. . . and this just about sums him up.

POOR OLD JONES...
HAS FUDGE GOT IT
IN FOR HIM...

FUDGE CORNERED HIM OVER BY THE
WINDOW AND STARTED RANTING AND
RAVING LIKE A MANIAC...

JONES BROKE CLEAR BUT FUDGE
CAUGHT HIM BY THE FILING CABINET
AND STARTED
ON HIM AGAIN...

SINCE THEN THEY'VE BEEN ALL
ROUND THE ROOM.....

WALL TO WALL CARPETING!

We know very little about him. We suspect he is married, but since he never brings his home to work we cannot be sure. (The reason for suspicion is that one night he invited the lads round for a game of cards and, upon their entrance, was seen to turn a framed photograph to the wall!) We cannot for certain say that this was Mrs Jones, and can therefore only assume this to be the better half.

It is surprising that a man possessing no imagination should continually show an interest in another man's activities, especially when that second man also lacks imagination, but Jones is nothing if not curious.

We know that he is a simple man, for he has been known to take advice from Bristow on the odd occasion, something a man in full possession of his faculties would not even contemplate, and we know he is red blooded for he likes to eat lunch in the park on a sunny day.

We also know that he is not particularly ambitious, since on one auspicious occasion he bowed to Bristow's insistence that he (Bristow) took precedence in all things because BRISTOW is first alphabetically, but we also know and realise he is indispensable to the strip, for he is the Perfect Straight Man.

8. MISS SUNMAN.

Miss Sunman, the faithful, long suffering link between Bristow *and the* Typing Pool, *is devoted to him. It is this lady who has for years been typing out his long* **exposé** *of office life,* **Living Death in the Buying Department** *in her own words and only altering the non-romantic parts to make them romantic, steamier, and thus more saleable.*

This is Miss Sunman.

Bristow, I regret to say, is not appreciative of his only fan and is inclined to run roughshod over her feelings.

Women, to Bristow, are an occupational hazard. Apart from the tea ladies, the cleaning staff and the Typing Pool (all of which are regarded as part of the furniture), the female of the species are an intrusion into the natural running of the place. Bristow, echoing George Bernard Shaw, believes that a woman should be pregnant, barefoot, and in the kitchen.

His views seem to be shared by at least one other member of the male staff.

To those lady readers who bombard me with angry letters vis-à-vis the comments expressed by these chauvinist white-collar pigs, I must hastily point out that these in no way express my own opinion. Who does George Bernard Shaw think he is? I ask.

9. WINDOWS.

Having explained to the best of my ability those characters that come into Bristow's immediate 'space', I will now venture into the area outside his desk.

Because he is fortunate to have a seat by the window, he can keep an eye on the world outside. The fact that this window faces that of the Myles & Rudge building is most convenient, since the staff are continually being replaced.

SURPRISE! SURPRISE!!

THERE'S THE GIRL THAT WORKS IN THE **OFFICE ACROSS THE STREET**...

IT'S THE FIRST TIME I'VE EVER SEEN HER OUT OF THE OFFICE......

UP TILL NOW SHE'S ALWAYS BEEN JUST A FACE AT THE WINDOW......

THERE'S A LOVELY RAINBOW OUT THERE...

SUPPOSED TO BE A CROCK OF GOLD WHERE THE RAINBOW ENDS....

OUT OF SHEER CURIOSITY LET ME JUST—

GOOD HEAVENS— IT'S **TRUE**!

IT FINISHES UP OUTSIDE THE ACCOUNTS!

Over the years, the window has given me hundreds of outlets for developing the strip. Bearing in mind the grass is always greener, Bristow can (and does) covet everything he sees in the office across the street, down to the last coconut macaroon.

He can watch the goings-on in the streets below, and at the present time is interested in shop doorways, where he has made of a rather dubious set of acquaintances who are sleeping rough.

But, and best of all, the window allows a few minutes of escape for Bristow, who still has a few hours to go to the end of another long day.

IN A KIND OF OFF-BEAT WAY I'VE GROWN QUITE ATTACHED TO THAT PLANT IN THE WINDOW BOX ACROSS THE STREET...

BY LEANING WELL BACK IN MY CHAIR, COVERING MY LEFT EYE AND SQUINTING THROUGH MY RIGHT FINGERS I CAN ELIMINATE ALL THE SURROUNDING BRICKWORK... ALL I CAN SEE IS A BUNCH OF COOL GREEN LEAVES....

SUDDENLY I'M MILES AWAY IN THE HEART OF THE COUNTRYSIDE....

10. TEA UP!

Mrs Purdy, the tea lady, has been serving up the goodness since time immemorial. Bristow accepts with a marked lack of grace and their exchanges are part of the daily ritual.

11. STRICTLY FOR THE BIRDS...

The bird put in an appearance on Bristow's sill about five years after the strip had started. It was meant to be a canary.

AS A RULE I DON'T HAVE ANYTHING TO DO WITH ANIMALS BUT THIS BIRD IS **DIFFERENT**.... WE HAVE SOMETHING IN COMMON

WE NEITHER OF US KNOW WHERE THE NEXT MEAL IS COMING FROM!

AH. YOUR FEATHERED FRIEND IS BACK.....
MMH!
WHAT A STRANGE EXPRESSION HE HAS ON HIS FACE....
MMMH.....
I USUALLY FEED HIM EVERY MORNING AT THIS TIME BUT TODAY I HAVEN'T BOTHERED...
HE'S PONDERING ON THE VAGARIES OF HUMAN NATURE........

FINDERS KEEPERS...
WHAT'S THAT, JONES?
LOOK WHAT I'VE FOUND ON YOUR WINDOW LEDGE...
A LITTLE MIRROR, A BELL AND A LADDER...
PUT THOSE BACK AT ONCE!
I BOUGHT THEM SPECIALLY FOR MY FEATHERED FRIEND......
TODAY HE WANTS TO PLAY AT BEING IN A CAGE......

ONE TEA AND THREE CAKES PLEASE.....
I THOUGHT MR. JONES WAS AWAY....
SO HE IS, BUT.........

MIAOW!
MIAOW!

GRRH!
SPRING

WHAT THE DEVIL IS BRISTOW DOING NOW ? HE'S BEEN STARING AT THAT BIRD FOR TEN MINUTES...
HE'S TRYING THOUGHT TRANSFERENCE.....
ORDER NUMBER DB 3959
FAT JUICY WORMS... CRUSTS OF BREAD...

BRISTOW — THE FACT THAT EVERYONE IN IN THE BUILDING IS SUFFERING FROM A COLD WON'T AFFECT YOUR FEATHERED FRIEND IN AT ALL....
IT IS A PROVEN MEDICAL FACT THAT CREATURES OF THE AIR ARE IMPERVIOUS TO THE ILLS COMMON TO MANKIND......
ATISHOO!

BRISTOW — YOUR FEATHERED FRIEND CANNOT HAVE A COLD... IT'S IMPOSSIBLE!!
JONES — HE'S BEEN COUGHING AND SNEEZING ALL MORNING — OF COURSE HE HAS A COLD....
HE'S A VICTIM OF ONE OF THE MANY ILLNESSES THAT FLESH IS HEIR TO....
OBSERVE THE WAY THE LEVEL OF GEE'S LINCTUS IN THAT SAUCER HAS GONE DOWN.....

I'VE BEEN GIVING SOME SERIOUS THOUGHT TO THIS ECOLOGY BUSINESS AND I'VE DECIDED TO GET A WINDOW BOX...
LANDSCAPED OF COURSE... A PLANT HERE... ROCKERY THERE.... A SHRUBBERY... A GLEAM OF WATER PERHAPS ?....
SHOO! SHOO!
HOW CAN I COMMUNE WITH NATURE WITH YOU IN THE WAY ?

12. FOOD, GLORIOUS FOOD...

Mr Gordon Blue, temperamental Master Chef of the Chester-Perry Canteen, has always been a particular favourite of mine. Followers of the strip will know of his addiction to cooking sherry and his dislike of tomato ketchup.

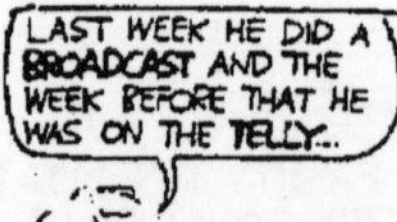

SOUP, BOILED FISH, MEAT PIE, TINNED PEARS...

MR. BLUE!—THE DIRECTORS WILL DINING ON THE PREMISES. WHAT WILL THEY BE EATING?

CONSOMME CELESTINE... SOLE VERONIQUE... GIGOT D'AGNEAU EN PÂTE POIRES BELLE HELENE....

BONJOUR MESSIEURS.... WHAT DO YOU THINK OF MY SAUTÉ D'AGNEAU AU PAPRIKA?
YUK!
MY SENTIMENTS EXACTLY..
STAND ASIDE, LADIES — LET ME SEE HOW MY CLIENTELE ARE ENJOYING TODAY'S SPECIALITY
CANTEEN
SACRE BLEUE! POITRINE DE BOEUF A LA NORMANDE SHOULD NOT HAVE BEEN ON TODAY'S MENU....
SOMEONE HAS BLUNDERED!

BON JOUR, MESSIEURS.
WELL, WELL, MR. GORDON BLUE, THE MASTER CHEF...
WHAT DO YOU THINK OF MY POULET EN COCOTTE BONNE FEMME?
DELICIOUS. WHAT SAY YOU: BRISTOW?
REMINDS ME OF SCHOOL DINNERS
SOB!
MOVE THE CRUET..

WHAT'S THAT PECULIAR HAMMERING SOUND EMANATING FROM THE FIRM'S CANTEEN?
YOU MEAN YOU HAVEN'T HEARD?
MR. GORDON BLUE HAS BEEN AWARDED YET ANOTHER STAR FROM THE 'FIRM'S CANTEEN GOOD FOOD GUIDE'
THE STRANGE NOISE IS THE MAN DRUMMING HIS HEELS WITH DELIGHT......

YOU KNOW, BRISTOW — WE MUST BE STUPID, EATING IN THE FIRM'S CANTEEN... WE'RE JUST GIVING THEM BACK THE MONEY WE WORK FOR...

NOT ONLY DO WE GIVE THEM THEIR MONEY BACK BUT THEY MAKE A FAT PROFIT OUT OF US...

AN EXTRAVAGANT CHEF LIKE MR. GORDON BLUE DOESN'T COME CHEAP, AFTER ALL...

THE FACT THAT HE CAN EXPERIMENT WITH DISHES LIKE POULET EN COCOTTE BONNE FEMME LEAVES A NASTY TASTE IN THE MOUTH.......
HOW TRUE — HOW VERY TRUE..

13. SCAFFOLDING TO THE GENTRY.

In the mid sixties the Blondini Brothers (Scaffolding to the Gentry) made their first appearance. Some years before, I had given up my job with Standard Telephones and Cables (Southgate) and was employed as a packer of women's hats in Commonwealth House in New Oxford Street. I noticed they were erecting some scaffolding across the road . . .

High above the Metropolis the Blondini Brothers (Scaffolding to the Gentry) are awaiting the arrival of two more intrepid spidermen.....
CERTAINLY NOT— ARE YOU OUT OF YOUR MIND?
I DON'T CARE HOW OLD THEY ARE...
SAFETY NETS ARE FOR GIRLS.....
BB
BB
BB
BB

YOU'RE NEW TO WALKING THE STEEL, AREN'T YOU?
FIRST DAY
REMEMBER THIS—THE GIRDERS ARE NINE INCHES WIDE..... DON'T GO NEAR THE EDGE.....

High above the Myles & Rudge building one of the Blondini Brothers (Scaffolding to the Gentry) is having an off day...

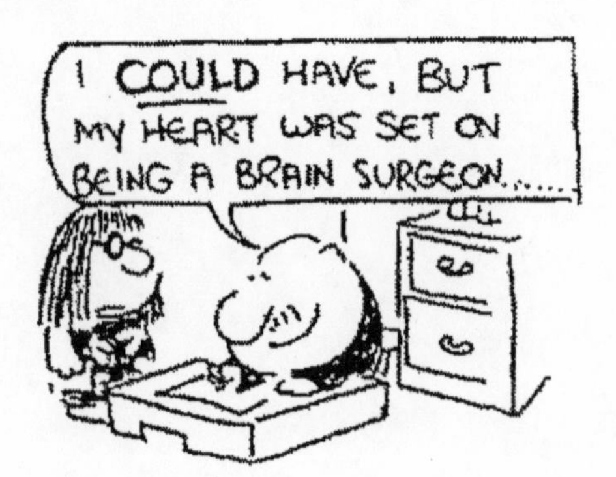

14. THE QUEENS OF SPICK 'N' SPAN.

Cleaning ladies are, to Bristow, back-room boys. He never meets them, and any communication exists courtesy of the dust on his desk top. He is generally scathing about their efforts, for he knows nothing of their world.

We outsiders, privy through the medium of the strip to their activities, must surely envy their attitude, not all of which is to do with the spick and span-ness for which they earn their bread 'n' butter.

The cleaners reciprocate his feelings and are prone to write hostile messages in the dust that they leave on his desk top.

They are openly scathing about the condition in which he leaves his desk and surrounds.

IT'S AMAZING HOW THESE OFFICES
HARBOUR THE **DUST**....
LOOK AT THE STATE OF THIS...

... AND IT'S ONLY
BEEN IN MY DRAWER
A FORTNIGHT...

15. BIG BROTHER.

The loudspeaker on the wall is one of my favourite accessories, constantly reminding employees that 'Big Brother' is not far away.

Some of its commands might seem out of place in a thriving modern organisation ('Maypole dancing on the spot', for example) but they go towards maintaining discipline of a kind and enable Sir Reginald to run a tight ship.

This message is obviously not to be taken seriously.

16. GETTING TO KNOW THE MAN

Looking back over what I have written so far, it seems to me that I have said very little about Bristow himself. Strange as it seems, even after ten thousand daily strips, I know nothing about him except that he is of indeterminate age, unmarried, and went to St Mary's Mixed Infants School. He appears to live in a bed-sit in East Winchley, but rarely do we see him there, unless he is about to leave for work.

THE VIEW FROM THIS WINDOW IS POSITIVELY BREATHTAKING!
FAR AWAY TO MY LEFT I CAN SEE THE CHESTER-PERRY BUILDING, LIKE A MATCHBOX ON THE HORIZON.... AND FAR AWAY TO MY RIGHT WHAT APPEARS TO BE A TOY TRAIN STEAMING INTO A MINIATURE STATION...
HOLY MACKEREL!!! — IT'S THE 8·15 COMMUTER SPECIAL —
LATE AGAIN!!!!!

On the odd occasion when he is caught off guard he is thinking over some great issue or other.

But his day really begins the moment he steps through the door and begins his walk to the station.

ALL THINGS CONSIDERED THIS ISN'T A BAD JOB... IT HAS IT'S UPS AND DOWNS, OF COURSE, BUT WHAT JOB HASN'T?

AND LET'S GIVE CREDIT WHERE IT'S DUE, THE MANAGEMENT ARE PRETTY FREE AND EASY...

WE CAN COME IN ANYTIME BEFORE NINE AND LEAVE ANYTIME AFTER FIVE.....

THERE'S NOTHING TO IT.....

A **GRUNT** FROM FUDGE MEANS IT IS **9.30** AM......

THE **RATTLE** OF CUPS AND SAUCERS MEANS IT IS **10.15**

THE **SIGHS** OF RELIEF MEAN IT IS **11.30**......

AND THE SOUNDS OF STAMPEDING FEET MEANS **FIVE MINUTES TO GO**..........

CLOCKWATCHING

BY EAR!

BRISTOW — WHAT IS THIS BAR FOR?
PSCYCHOLOGY.
PSCYCHOLOGY?
WHENEVER YOU ARE FILLED WITH A BURNING DESIRE TO WALK OUT YOU GRAB IT AND HANG ON TILL THE MOMENT'S PASSED....

JONES — SINCE WE ARE BEING PERFECTLY FRANK WITH EACH OTHER, WOULD YOU MIND IF I ASK YOU A PERSONAL QUESTION?
THAT DEPENDS...
IS IT NORMAL PERSONAL, MEDIUM PERSONAL, OR SMACK-IN-THE-MOUTH PERSONAL?

TAKE THIS REQUISITION TO MR. BRISTOW IN THE BUYING DEPARTMENT...
MR. BRISTOW?
HE'S SULKING —TRY THE BROOM CUPBOARD...
MR. BRISTOW?
KNOCK! KNOCK!
GO AWAY....

YOU HAVEN'T DONE ALL THESE TODAY?
OUT
YES....I WAS TIRED OF SEEING THEM TAKING UP SO MUCH SPACE AND DECIDED TO GET CRACKING ON THEM....
OUT
DREAM ON........
OUT

I'M TRYING TO RAISE SOME MONEY FOR CHARITY... WILL YOU **SPONSOR** ME?
WHAT ARE YOU GOING TO DO?
I'M GOING TO ATTEMPT A FULL DAYS WORK.....

IS IT TRUE YOU'RE BEING **SPONSORED** TO ATTEMPT A FULL DAYS WORK?
THAT'S RIGHT...
DO YOU THINK YOU CAN DO IT?
I DON'T SEE WHY NOT....
ALL I HAVE TO DO IS STAY AWAKE

IS IT TRUE MR. BRISTOW IS ATTEMPTING A FULL DAYS WORK?
YUP.
WILL HE DO IT?
HE WILL IF HE DOESN'T FALL ASLEEP
WHERE IS HE?
HE'S IN THE CLOAKROOM WITH HIS HEAD UNDER THE COLD WATER TAP...

I CAN'T UNDERSTAND.... HOW COME I THINK OF A BRILLIANT IDEA AND FIND SOMEONE HAS ALREADY THOUGHT OF IT?

NOT ONLY **THOUGHT** OF IT — THEY'VE **IMPROVED** IT, **REFINED** IT — AND IT'S IN **EVERYDAY USE**...

WHEN I THOUGHT OF THE **WHEEL** THAT TIME, I HAD NO IDEA.......

I'VE JUST DISCOVERED SOMETHING TERRIBLE ABOUT MYSELF....
I CAN'T BELIEVE IT!

WITHOUT EVEN THINKING I SAT DOWN AT MY DESK, PICKED UP A PEN AND STARTED WRITING..... JUST LIKE THAT! IT WAS AUTOMATIC!! AND I KNOW WHAT IT MEANS......

I'VE GOT CLERICAL GENES..

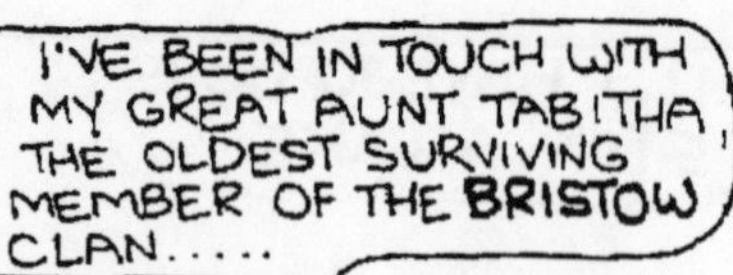
I'VE BEEN IN TOUCH WITH MY GREAT AUNT TABITHA, THE OLDEST SURVIVING MEMBER OF THE BRISTOW CLAN.....

SHE SAYS IF I HAVE ANY CLERICAL GENES IN MY BLOOD THEY COULD ONLY HAVE BEEN PASSED DOWN FROM THE ONLY WORKAHOLIC IN THE FAMILY, WHO HELD DOWN AN OFFICE JOB FOR 25 YEARS....

THEY CALLED HIM 'CRAZY LEW'....

I DIDN'T KNOW YOU WERE LEFT HANDED, BRISTOW...
I'M NOT, AS A RULE...
WELL, WHAT'S THE MATTER WITH YOUR RIGHT HAND?
Z

I WATCHED A REMARKABLE PROGRAMME ON 'WHITE COLLAR T.V.' LAST NIGHT....
IN SOME FAR FLUNG CORNER OF THE UNIVERSE A BAND OF ARCHAEOLOGISTS HAVE COME ACROSS THE REMAINS OF A PREVIOUS CIVILISATION...
A TOMB SURROUNDED BY THIRTY THOUSAND TERRA COTTA BUYING CLERKS.....
YOU FIND THAT REMARKABLE?
BEEN THERE. DONE THAT, GOT THE T SHIRT

DID THEY DO THE CHESTER-PERRY BARBEQUE-ON-THE-ROOF THIS YEAR?
LET'S SEE.... HOW CAN I PUT IT?
NEWS OF THE EAST WING BEING BURNT DOWN HASN'T REACHED YOU, YET?

SIR — THIS FIRM TRICKED ME INTO WORKING HERE..
THERE'S NOTHING ABOUT CRUELTY IN THE CHESTER-PERRY TERMS OF EMPLOYMENT.....
YOU ARE WRONG — READ THEM AGAIN — BUT THIS TIME READ THEM CAREFULLY....
THEY MENTION CRUELTY IN THE SMALL PRINT...

WHERE ARE YOU GOING FOR THIS HOLIDAY?
I DON'T KNOW — IT'S A WALKING HOLIDAY
DON'T BE SILLY...
JONES — YOU CAN'T GO ON A WALKING HOLIDAY....
I'M NOT BEING SILLY...
HOW ARE WE GOING TO GET YOUR WORK OUT TO YOU...?
RUN AFTER ME...

THIS IS VERY PLEASANT, BRISTOW THE STIRRING OF THE BLOOD AND QUICKENING OF THE PULSE, WITH THE REALISATION THAT SPRING IS HERE...
I LOVE THE EARLY MONTHS... WHEN CROCUSES, SNOWDROPS AND DAFFODILS SHOW THEIR PRETTY FACES.... WHEN TREES GAILY CLOTHE THEMSELVES IN THEIR GREENERY AND TINY LAMBS GAMBOL IN THE MEADOWS..
WHAT'S YOUR FAVOURITE MONTH?
ANY MONTH WITH FIVE PAYDAYS IN IT.......

WHAT A BEAUTIFUL WORD PROCESSOR....... SO SMALL... SO COMPACT...
CERTAINLY IS — I DON'T GO ANYWHERE WITHOUT IT... FEEL THE WEIGHT.....
MARVELLOUS! IS IT COMPLICATED?
NOT REALLY —THERE'S ALLWAYS THE INSTRUCTION MANUAL.....

LETTER TO MESSRS. GUN & FAMES 'DEAR SIR, OUR ORDER NUMBER DB 2392. THE ABOVE ORDER WAS URGED BY US ON 20TH ULTIMO BUT NO REPLY HAS BEEN RECEIVED.
PERHAPS YOU WILL HAVE THE COURTESY TO ANSWER THIS TIME, YOU LAZY, SLOTHFUL, GOOD-FOR-NOTHING PIG!
IF A REPLY HAS BEEN SENT DURING THE LAST SEVEN DAYS KINDLY DISREGARD THIS LETTER...

WHAT A PERFECT DAY...
A CLOUDLESS SKY
OF AZURE BLUE...
BRILLIANT SUNSHINE...
AND TO CROWN IT ALL IF I OPEN THE WINDOW
THERE'S JUST THE RIGHT AMOUNT OF BREEZE...
IN
OUT

I'M TRYING A NEW EXPERIENCE TO EASE EVERYDAY TENSIONS.... HEAD TO TOE RELAXATION... WORKING MY WAY RIGHT UP MY BODY... EASY DOES IT... EASY NOW... MY **TOES** ARE RELAXED... MY **LEGS** ARE RELAXED... MY **BODY** IS RELAXED... NOW MY **ARMS** AND **HANDS**.. NOW MY **FINGERS**... EASY DOES IT... EEESSY BOY... NOW MY **EYES**... NOW MY **BRAIN**..... BLANKNESS....... BLANKNESS..... **BLANKNESS**.... THAT'S IT! I'M READY!

PASS ME THE INVOICES!

WHAT'S THE MATTER, MR. BRISTOW?
THE MUSIC HAS STARTED...
JONES COMES BACK FROM HIS HOLIDAYS NEXT WEEK....
YOU MENTIONED MUSIC.....
YES.....YOU KNOW HOW IN HORROR FILMS YOU HEAR MUSIC JUST BEFORE SOMETHING DREADFUL HAPPENS....?

WHO? WHO? WHO? IT'S DRIVING ME CRAZY...
I RECEIVED A VALENTINE CARD AND I'D LIKE TO KNOW WHO SENT IT...
SIGH! YOU HAVE THE SAME TROUBLE EVERY YEAR —WHY DON'T YOU DO WHAT I DO?
GET IT FINGERPRINTED.....

SSH! DON'T SPEAK....
BRISTOW IS BEING CARPETTED— LISTEN...!
I (SLAP!) SHAN'T (SLAP!) TELL (SLAP!) YOU (SLAP!) AGAIN (SLAP!)

WHAT ON EARTH IS THE MATTER WITH BRISTOW?
TAKE NO NOTICE..... HE'S GOING THROUGH HIS DROWNING MAN ROUTINE.....
HE CLAIMS EVERY TIME HE SITS DOWN AT HIS DESK HIS WHOLE PAST LIFE FLASHES BEFORE HIM

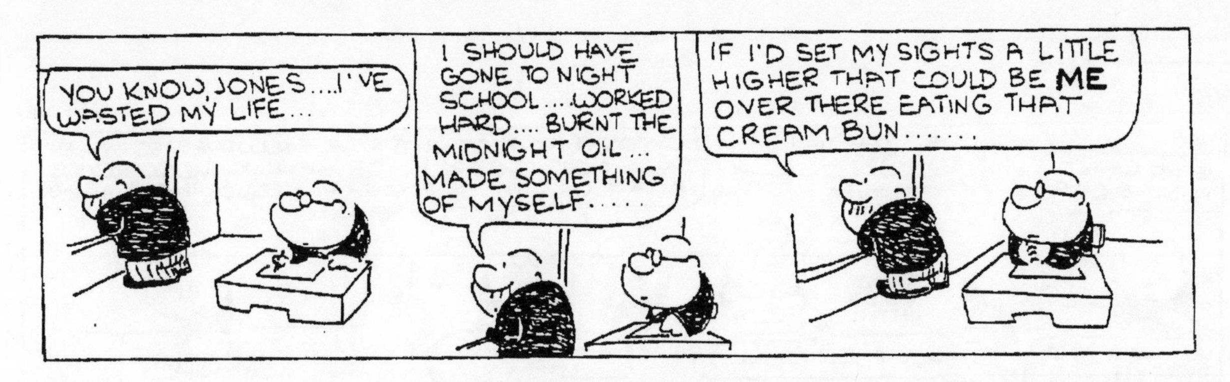
YOU KNOW, JONES....I'VE WASTED MY LIFE...
I SHOULD HAVE GONE TO NIGHT SCHOOL....WORKED HARD.... BURNT THE MIDNIGHT OIL... MADE SOMETHING OF MYSELF.....
IF I'D SET MY SIGHTS A LITTLE HIGHER THAT COULD BE **ME** OVER THERE EATING THAT CREAM BUN.......

WHAT ON EARTH IS THAT.?
THUMP! THUMP!
IT'S SIR REGINALD CHESTER —PERRY'S LATEST IDEA....
THUMP! THUMP! THUMP!
YOU KNOW HOW IN ROMAN GALLEYS THEY USED TO BEAT OUT A RHYTHM FOR THE SLAVES THAT WERE ROWING......? HOLY MACKEREL —THIS IS **RAMMING** SPEED!
THUMP! THUMP! THUMP! THUMP! THUMP!

I'D LOVE TO WRITE FOR THE FIRM'S HOUSE JOURNAL....
IN HEAVEN'S NAME —WHY?
IF YOU WRITE ANYTHING THAT GETS PUBLISHED YOUR NAME AUTOMATICALLY GOES ON THE FIRM'S **ROLL** OF **HONOUR**....

ARE YOU THE **HEADHUNTER** THAT'S BEEN CHASING ME AROUND ?
KNOCK THREE TIMES ON THE CARTON IF YOU READ ME — TWICE ON THE STEP IF THE ANSWER IS NO.........

IS MR. GAVIN AVAILABLE ...?
NO — HE'S AT A MEETING......
HE'S ALWAYS AT A MEETING....
HE'S A BUSY MAN....
BUSY MAN, MY FOOT... THESE MEETINGS ARE A TAKE ON.....
IT'S THE EXECUTIVE'S EQUNALENT OF WALKING THE CORRIDORS WITH A PIECE OF PAPER IN MY HAND...

WOULD YOU BELIEVE IT? — I'VE COME OUT WITHOUT MY PEN...
HAVE MINE.....
BUT WON'T YOU BE WANTING IT YOURSELF TO TAKE NOTES ?
YES MEN DON'T NEED NOTES.........

IT'S A LOVELY DAY, BRISTOW — WHAT'S IT TO BE, LUNCH IN THE PARK, OR THE CANTEEN?
I THINK THE CANTEEN...
IN THE CANTEEN YOU CAN TAKE YOUR SHIRT OFF WITHOUT PEOPLE STARING.....

YOU WANT TO KNOW HOW TO WRITE A THREATENING LETTER? STAND BACK AND I'LL DEMONSTRATE...
DEMONSTRATE ?
CERTAINLY... YOU DON'T MIND A BIT OF NOISE?
NOISE?
I ALWAYS SHOUT ALOUD WHEN WRITING A THREATENING LETTER.... BACK A BIT... BIT MORE.

YOUR STAFF HAVE BEEN VERY LAX IN DEALING WITH THIS...

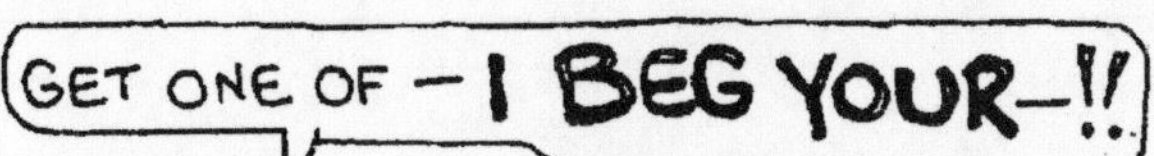
GET ONE OF — I BEG YOUR—!!

LICK!
LICK!

YOU'LL PROBABLY LAUGH AT THIS BUT FOR ONE MOMENT I THOUGHT.....

WHAT'S YOUR HAT DOING ON THE WINDOW LEDGE?
I'M USING IT AS A SUN DIAL.....
YOU MEAN YOU CAN TELL THE TIME BY THAT? HOW DOES IT WORK?
EASY.....
IF I WANT TO KNOW THE TIME I STAND UP AND REACH FOR IT LIKE THIS...
BRISTOW – GET BACK TO YOUR DESK – IT'S ONLY TEN TO TWELVE!
NEVER FAILS...

GOOD HEAVENS! DID YOU SEE THAT?
THE HANDS ON THAT CLOCK LITERALLY JUMPED TWO WHOLE MINUTES...
FROM TEN PAST TEN TO TWELVE MINUTES PAST...
TWO WHOLE MINUTES OF MY LIFE GONE– JUST LIKE THAT!
IT STOPPED ME DEAD IN MY TRACKS. I CAN TELL YOU, SEEING THAT HAND JUMP LIKE THAT...
FOR A MOMENT TIME STOOD STILL........

WHAT'S THE TIME, BRISTOW?
LET'S SEE– WHERE'S MY WASTE-PAPER BASKET?
JUST OVER TWO INCHES TO GO...
HALF PAST FOUR!

I NEED A SPOT OF HELP MISS SUNMAN
THEY'VE JUST GIVEN ME A NEW WASTEPAPER BASKET...
I'M GOING TO SIGN MY NAME ON THE BOTTOM.....
I SEE — AND YOU WANT ME TO — ?
EXACTLY..
WITNESSED THIS THIRD DAY....

PASS THE TOMATO SAUCE, PLEASE....
GOOD HEAVENS.— HOUGHTON OF ST. MARY'S MIXED INFANTS.!! YOU REMEMBER ME — BRISTOW ? I'M THE BOY WHO ACCUSED YOU OF STEALING HIS SCHOOL CAP....
SO IT IS........ BRISTOW! HOW ON EARTH DID YOU RECOGNISE ME AFTER ALL THESE YEARS?
I NEVER FORGET A FIST......

WELL, WELL, HOW NICE TO SEE YOU AGAIN AFTER ALL THESE YEARS — AND HERE OF ALL PLACES! IT'S A SMALL WORLD, ISN'T IT?
IT IS INDEED A SMALL WORLD, IT IS INDEED.......
AH, WELL, MUST GET BACK TO THE OFFICE... CHEERIO, BRISTOW... NO DOUBT WE'LL MEET AGAIN....
HE MUST BE OUT OF HIS MIND.... MEET AGAIN?
... IN A CANTEEN THIS SIZE?

WHEN DID I LOSE INTEREST IN THE FIRM? I SUPPOSE YOU COULD SAY THE FIRST DAY...
THE MOMENT I WALKED INTO THE BUILDING A LITTLE THING CALLED ENTHUSIASM DIED.....

BLUE SKIES ... BRILLIANT SUNSHINE... FLOWERS BURSTING FROM THEIR WINDOW BOXES... FAREWELL COLD WINTER!

OH, TO BE A SALES REP. NOW THAT SPRING IS HERE.....

WHATEVER YOU GUYS ARE PLANNING I WANT TO COME IN ON IT....

WE DIDN'T ASK YOU TO COME IN WITH US BECAUSE WE DON'T THINK YOU CAN CONTRIBUTE ANYTHING...
WHO SAYS I CAN'T?

THE BALLET AIN'T OVER TILL THE SWAN DIES.....

MORNING, MR. SAMPSON
MORNING MY DEAR.
USUAL?
YES PLEASE.
HOW WOULD YOU LIKE IT?
FIVES PLEASE.
SOB!

WHAT'S IT LIKE, BEING A SALES REP.?

WHAT'S IT LIKE?? WELL, ER, IT'S ER.. HOW CAN I SAY? ER...WELL, HOW CAN I DESCRIBE IT?
ER, IT'S.. WELL.. NOW HOW SHALL I PUT IT?

IT'S-ER- YOU KNOW IT'S... WELL... IT'S...

YOU'VE GOT TO HAVE THE GIFT OF THE GAB....

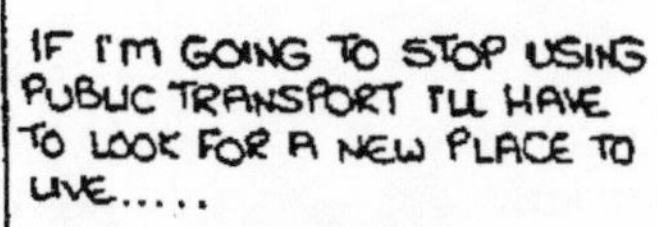

IF I'M GOING TO STOP USING PUBLIC TRANSPORT I'LL HAVE TO LOOK FOR A NEW PLACE TO LIVE.....

SOMEWHERE CLOSER TO THE HEART OF. THINGS...

I'D LIKE A NICE, ROOMY BACHELOR PAD IN TOWN......

WITHIN A STONE'S THROW OF THE CHESTER-PERRY BUILDING.........

WHAT DO YOU MEAN — NO BISCUITS? DOESN'T IT EVER OCCUR TO YOU PEOPLE TO PUT MORE ON THE TROLLEY?
HAVEN'T GOT ROOM, LOVE.
HAVEN'T GOT ROOM? HAVEN'T GOT **ROOM**?? COME WITH ME
IF THE SURFACE AREA OF A TEA TROLLEY IS 3' x 2' AND THE AVERAGE BISCUIT MEASURES $2\frac{1}{2}$" x $1\frac{3}{8}$" ....

CHESTER-PERRY'S 'BAR-B-Q ON THE ROOF' IS OPENING TODAY...
RIGHT HAND DOWN

SICK BAY
NURSE! NURSE!
I'VE JUST WORKED OUT WHAT IT TAKES TO GET TO THE TOP...
I'D LIKE SOMETHING TO STOP MY MIND BOGGLING.....

GET THAT COUGH SEEN TO, BRISTOW....
COUGH INDEED! THE MAN'S A FOOL....
HE CAN'T EVEN RECOGNISE A MUTINOUS DOG SNARLING AT HIM....
GRRR!

BRISTOW—THAT BOOK 'TOWARDS A FLAT STOMACH' IS OF NO USE TO YOU....
YOU NEED THE 'CHESTER-PERRY GUIDE TO HEALTH AND WELL BEING'...
IT'LL PUT A SPRING IN YOUR STEP AND BRING A SPARKLE TO YOUR EYES.....
MOST KIND...
SIT DOWN, PICK UP PEN, WORK HARD FOR EIGHT HOURS....

17. COMING UP FOR AIR...

In an earlier passage I mentioned that Bristow lived in a bed-sit in East Winchley and that he is seldom seen at home.

It came as a surprise to me to find, when sorting out the strips for this opus, that I had completely forgotten his landlady, Mrs Peel and the previous resident of his room, a Mr Tipple. (Perhaps too much of the latter blotted out memories of the former!)

We have now met, albeit briefly, most of the regular main characters that appear in the strip. Apart from the characters there are a number of, for want of a better word, 'themes' that crop up from time to time, that a new reader will not be familiar with.

Let's put in a few here . . .

SO THAT GIRL OVER THERE HAS MOVED INTO A BED SIT. OPPOSITE YOU..?
THAT'S RIGHT....
HERE'S A MAP... YOUR BED. SIT IS ON THE NORTH SIDE... HERS IS ON THE SOUTH.....?
THAT'S RIGHT.... BUT WHAT'S ON YOUR MIND?
IF YOU PLAY YOUR CARDS RIGHT YOU WON'T HAVE SO FAR TO COME TO WORK IN THE MORNINGS...

AREN'T YOU AFRAID OF GOING IN TO SEE FUDGE WITH SUCH A FLIMSY EXCUSE?
AFRAID? NO..... NERVOUS. YES... BUT WHY SHOULD I BE AFRAID?...
THERE'S A TEAM OF MEDICS STANDING BY .....

DAMN THESE CLEANING LADIES! THEY'VE MOVED OUR DESKS CLOSER TOGETHER...
AM I SPEAKING TOO LOUD?
SORT OF...
EVERY TIME YOU SPEAK THE MAN IN THE OFFICE ACROSS THE STREET NODS HIS HEAD.

WHAT IS THE TITLE OF YOUR TELEVISION PLAY?
IT'S UNNAMED AT PRESENT.. TITLES ARE DIFFICULT TO COME UP WITH....
WHEN I FIRST ARRIVE IN THE MORNING I CALL IT 'CALL THIS LIVING?'
AFTER TEA BREAK IT'S 'LIFE IS JUST A BOWL OF CHERRIES..'

BRITISH HI-SPEED RAIL ARE ADVERTISING FOR STATION STAFF.......
GO FOR IT...
NO POINT...
ONLY THOSE WITH A KNOWLEDGE OF PRISON REGIME NEED APPLY.

MEAT PIE AND POTATOES, PLEASE.....
MENU
THE CHEF HERE IS A PERSONAL FRIEND OF MINE.....
MENU
MEAT PIE WITH EXTRA POTATOES.......

HOW PLEASANT TO STROLL BY THE CANAL AS IT FLOWS GENTLY DOWN TO THE SEA..
FLOWS GENTLY DOWN TO THE SEA MY FOOT! IT CAN HARDLY MOVE WITH THE AMOUNT OF JUNK AND RUBBISH PEOPLE HAVE CHUCKED INTO IT...
THE NAUTICAL EQUIVALENT OF A WASTEPAPER BASKET...

I'M NOT PUTTING ON WEIGHT, I'M NOT !!
HOW CAN I BE PUTTING ON WEIGHT? I'M EATING THE SAME THINGS — DOING THE SAME THINGS... I CAN'T BE!
SIGH! FOR THE THIRD TIME TODAY...
I SPEAK YOUR WEIGHT

Lunch in the park should be a regular theme but due to the vagaries of the British weather the days on which this is possible are limited.

LOT OF CHESTER-PERRY PEOPLE IN THE PARK TODAY...

YOU CAN TELL A CHESTER-PERRY MAN A MILE OFF...
HE'S THE BROWBEATEN ONE WITH THE SAD FACE...THE HANGDOG EXPRESSION AND THE NERVOUS TWITCH....

THE CHESTER-PERRY TRADEMARK....
TWITCH! TWITCH!

BRRH!
BRRH!
BRRH!
BRRH!
CAN'T TALK NOW — I'M IN CONFERENCE....

I'VE WASTED ENOUGH TIME ON THIS ORDER AND IT'S BEGINNING TO SERIOUSLY INCONVENIENCE ME..
I WANTED TO GO OUT FOR LUNCH TODAY...

ISN'T NATURE WONDERFUL?
UH HUH!
THE GREEN OF THE TREES, THE BLUE OF THE SKY, THE QUACKING OF THE DUCKS, THE BUZZING OF INNUMERABLE BEES_
IT ALL MEANS SOMETHING, Y'KNOW_ EVERYTHING HAS A PURPOSE...
HOW TRUE_ HOW VERY TRUE....
WHAT DOES IT MEAN WHEN THE GEESE FLY SOUTH?
TIME WE WERE GETTING BACK TO WORK!!!

WELL, I MUST BE GETTING BACK TO WORK... THIS LUNCHING IN THE PARK IS ALL VERY WELL BUT...
ER – I HAVEN'T A GREAT DEAL OF MONEY ON ME — WE DON'T GET PAID TILL THIS AFTER—
PLEASE – DON'T EMBARRASS ME – BEING AN OLD CHESTER-PERRY MAN MYSELF, I WOULDN'T DREAM OF ACCEPTING IT ANYWAY...
TELL YOU SOMETHING THOUGH, THAT COPY OF THE HOUSE JOURNAL...
TAKE IT, PLEASE... NICE TO THINK AN OLD CHESTER-PERRY MAN IS STILL INTERESTED IN THE FIRM...
GOD BLESS YOU...
SEE YOU AROUND THEN...

WELL, WELL, 'HI-TECH' HICKS — WHAT'S NEW?
WORD PROCESSOR... FAX.... SCANNER...... YOU NAME IT — I'VE GOT IT....
AND FOUR 'PHONES... WHY FOUR?
HELP LINE FOR THE FAX... HELP LINE FOR THE WORD PROCESSOR... HELP LINE FOR THE SCANNER....

I DID IT! I'VE CLEARED MY IN-TRAY!
YOU HEAR THAT JONES?
I DID IT!
I'M UP TO DATE — I'M ON TOP OF EVERYTHING!
SLAP!

FRANKLY, I DON'T KNOW WHAT WE CAN DO ABOUT IT.
WHAT ON EARTH...?
IT'S PAST IT'S DO-BY DATE.....

Somewhere in the Sahara Desert....
WHAT IS IT, SERGEANT PIG?
IT'S LEGIONNAIRE SMITH, MON CAPITAN..
HE WISHES TO RESIGN FROM THE LEGION AND BECOME A BUYING CLERK....
SACRE BLEUE! PLACE HIM UNDER CLOSE ARREST...
TEN DAYS IN THE HOT HOLE SHOULD BRING HIM TO HIS SENSES.....

NINE FIFTEEN....
YAWN!
PRELIMINARIES OVER....
TIME TO GET THE TOYS OUT

HOUGHTON HAS BEEN WITH THE FIRM TWENTY FIVE YEARS — THEY ARE MAKING THE PRESENTATION TOMORROW...
GOLD WATCH?
ARE YOU KIDDING?
AT THIS FIRM?
FOR TWENTY FIVE YEARS IT'S A BOOK TOKEN OR A LUNCHEON VOUCHER......

BRISTOW IS AN INNOVATOR....
AMONG MANY OTHER THINGS HE PERFECTED THE LAID-BACK-WITH-EYES-CLOSED POSITION ADOPTED BY PEN-PUSHERS THE WORLD OVER....

SO, AS EDITOR OF THE HOUSE JOURNAL YOU PUT A LOT OF YOURSELF INTO THE MAGAZINE?
I SUPPOSE YOU COULD SAY THAT, REALLY
I VOICE A GREAT MANY OPINIONS AND, WITHOUT BEING IMMODEST, MAKE A GREAT NUMBER OF PEOPLE SQUIRM....
THE PEN IS MIGHTIER THAN THE SWORD, REMEMBER.
HO! HO! HO!
MIND YOU — I DON'T GO AS FAR AS TO PUT MY JOB IN JEOPARDY....
I SEE...
IN YOUR CASE THE PEN IS MIGHTIER THAN THE SWORD BUT NOT HALF AS MIGHTY AS THE AXE.......
HO! HO! HO! HO!

HAVE YOU BEEN AT THAT SAME DESK FOR TWENTY FIVE YEARS?
YUP!
IN THE SAME SPOT?
NO — MY DESK WAS OVER THERE TILL THE GREAT TEA TROLLEY DISASTER OF '76
AFTER THAT EVERYONE IN THE BUILDING WAS SHUFFLED ROUND.......

WHAT'S GOING ON?
TWITTER! TWITTER! TWITTER! TWITTER! TWITTER!
YOU WON'T GET MUCH WORK FROM THE TYPING POOL THIS WEEK......
TWITTER! TWITTER! TWITTER! TWITTER!
WE'VE GOT THE BUILDERS IN.......
TWITTER! TWITTER! TWITTER! TWITTER!

WHY HAVE WE GOT THE BUILDERS IN?
OBVIOUSLY YOU HAVEN'T HEARD...
THEY ARE HERE TO BRICK UP THE ESCAPE TUNNEL.....

GOOD DAY, GENTLEMEN... HOW ARE WE ENJOYING THE BOEUF STROGANOFF?
LET'S PUT IT THIS WAY — IT WAS SAVED BY THE TOMATO KETCHUP
HEAR HEAR
PEASANTS!
GOOD DAY SIR... AND HOW IS THE POULET EN COCOTTE BONNE FEMME?
WHAT CAN I SAY? WHAT CAN I SAY?
THE LAST TIME I TASTED FOOD LIKE THIS WAS IN A RESTAURANT ON THE MOTORWAY......
SOB!

YOU'D BEST SIT DOWN BEFORE YOU FALL DOWN...
THANK YOU, JONES...
HAVE YOU RUN ALL THE WAY FROM THE STATION AGAIN
UH HUH
YOU'VE DONE IT EVERY DAY FOR SIX WEEKS
UH HUH!
HAVE ANY HEADHUNTERS PHONED ASKING FOR ME ?

LET'S FACE IT, I'M OUT OF TOUCH... I MEAN COMPLETELY! I DON'T KNOW WHAT'S GOING ON....
I WENT TO A DINNER PARTY LAST NIGHT...
THEY WERE TALKING ABOUT ORDINARY THINGS AND I WAS STRUGGLING TO KEEP UP MY END OF THE CONVERSATION....

SO THESE ARE THE DRAWINGS FOR THE NEW WORD PROCESSOR?
THAT'S RIGHT, SIR
WHAT'S THIS THING ON THE SIDE?
A BUILT-IN ANTI-DESK RAGE BUTTON......

YOU KNOW YOUR TROUBLE, JONES? YOU HAVEN'T DECIDED EXACTLY WHAT YOU WANT OUT OF LIFE...
YES I HAVE — I WANT MONEY, FAME AND POWER....
LAUDABLE, JONES... HIGHLY LAUDABLE...
AND I'M SURE IT WILL HAPPEN IF YOU KEEP PLUGGING AWAY....

KEEP STILL A MINUTE.
YES.... AUTUMN, SEASON OF MISTS AND MELLOW FRUITFULNESS IS WITH US......
HIS FEATHERS ARE TURNING TO RUSSET AND GOLD.........

HAVE YOU FINISHED WITH MY DATE STAMP YET, BRISTOW?
DATE STAMP, JONES?
YES. I SEEM TO REMEMBER YOUR PUTTING IT AWAY IN THE TOP RIGHT HAND CORNER OF YOUR DESK.
BY JINGO! YOU ARE RIGHT! WHEN DID I BORROW THAT?
BREATHE! BREATHE!
MMMMH!
8 AUG 1995....

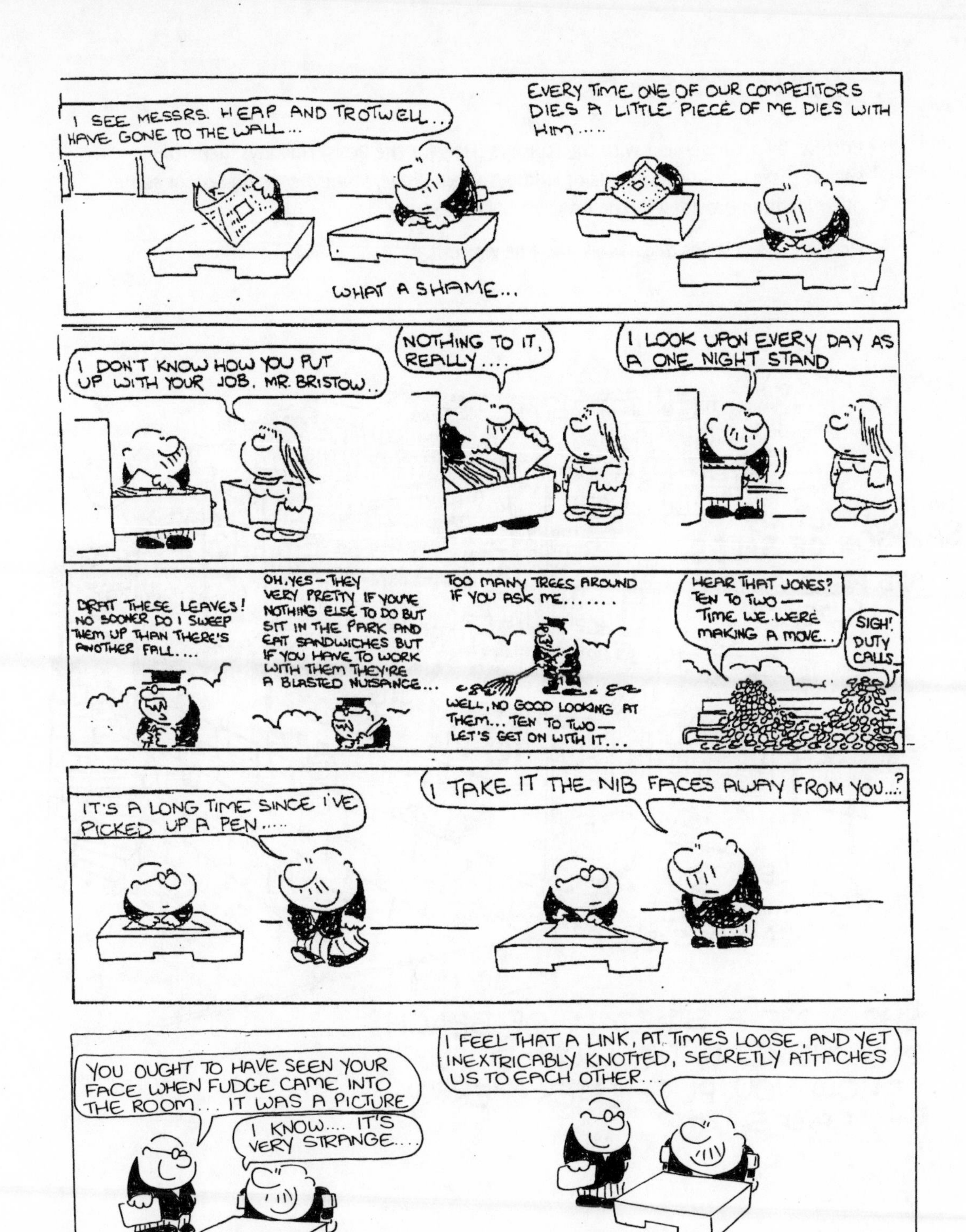
I SEE MESSRS. HEAP AND TROTWELL... HAVE GONE TO THE WALL...
WHAT A SHAME...
EVERY TIME ONE OF OUR COMPETITORS DIES A LITTLE PIECE OF ME DIES WITH HIM.....
I DON'T KNOW HOW YOU PUT UP WITH YOUR JOB, MR. BRISTOW..
NOTHING TO IT, REALLY....
I LOOK UPON EVERY DAY AS A ONE NIGHT STAND
DRAT THESE LEAVES! NO SOONER DO I SWEEP THEM UP THAN THERE'S ANOTHER FALL....
OH, YES - THEY VERY PRETTY IF YOU'RE NOTHING ELSE TO DO BUT SIT IN THE PARK AND EAT SANDWICHES BUT IF YOU HAVE TO WORK WITH THEM THEY'RE A BLASTED NUISANCE...
TOO MANY TREES AROUND IF YOU ASK ME.......
WELL, NO GOOD LOOKING AT THEM... TEN TO TWO - LET'S GET ON WITH IT...
HEAR THAT JONES? TEN TO TWO - TIME WE WERE MAKING A MOVE..
SIGH! DUTY CALLS
IT'S A LONG TIME SINCE I'VE PICKED UP A PEN.....
I TAKE IT THE NIB FACES AWAY FROM YOU...?
YOU OUGHT TO HAVE SEEN YOUR FACE WHEN FUDGE CAME INTO THE ROOM... IT WAS A PICTURE
I KNOW.... IT'S VERY STRANGE....
I FEEL THAT A LINK, AT TIMES LOOSE, AND YET INEXTRICABLY KNOTTED, SECRETLY ATTACHES US TO EACH OTHER...

18. HELLO, SAILORS!

Bristow, by arrangement with the Funboys (Hols for the Prols) Holidays, generally *spends these glorious moments at* Funboys-sur-la-Plage, Stoneybeach-on-Sea, *or some* other location *provided by the* brothers Sol and Sonny.

Here are a few strips taken while the tide was out.

WHERE ARE YOU GOING, BRISTOW?
I'M OFF TO SEE WHAT JONES IS UP TO.
I DIDN'T REALISE HE CAME ON HOLIDAY WITH YOU...

HE DIDN'T!
GIANT TELESCOPE

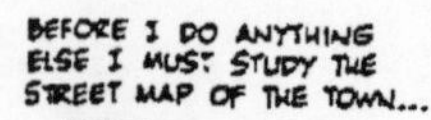

BEFORE I DO ANYTHING ELSE I MUST STUDY THE STREET MAP OF THE TOWN...
GET MY BEARINGS, SO TO SPEAK...

FUNNY, REALLY — THERE'S SOMETHING FAMILIAR ABOUT THIS LAYOUT... I FEEL I KNOW IT ALREADY...

BANK THERE... RESTAURANT THERE... TELEPHONE EXCHANGE NEXT DOOR... SECRETARIAL COLLEGE ALONG THE STREET...

HOLY MACKEREL! — THIS TOWN IS A SCALED-DOWN VERSION OF THE CHESTER-PERRY BUILDING!!

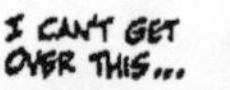
I CAN'T GET OVER THIS...

I'VE COME ON HOLIDAY TO STONEYBEACH-ON-SEA TO GET AWAY FROM IT ALL AND I STILL FEEL I'M BACK AT WORK...

THIS HOTEL IS EXACTLY THE SAME AS THE CHESTER-PERRY BUILDING...
NOT ONLY THAT BUT THE ROOM THEY'VE GIVEN ME IS ON THE SAME FLOOR AS MY OFFICE AND THE FURNITURE IN THE SAME PLACE

IF I SUBSTITUTED A DESK FOR THIS BED AND A FILING CABINET FOR THIS CHEST OF DRAWERS IT'D BE THE BUYING DEPARTMENT TO A TEE...

RIGHT DOWN TO THE GULL ON MY WINDOW LEDGE...

HEY, MUM — LOOK AT THAT MAN ON THE DIVING BOARD...
HE'S CLIMBED TO THE VERY TOP BOARD...

HE'S GOT MORE NERVE THAN I HAVE...
MUST BE SOME KIND OF INTERNATIONAL DIVER, I SUPPOSE

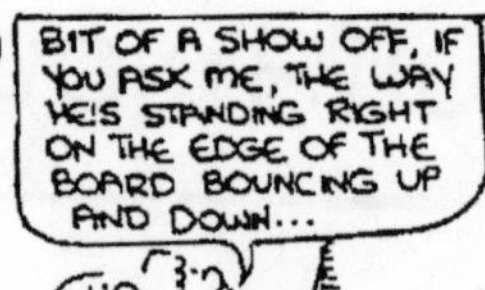
BIT OF A SHOW OFF, IF YOU ASK ME, THE WAY HE'S STANDING RIGHT ON THE EDGE OF THE BOARD BOUNCING UP AND DOWN...

I KNEW IT — FROM HERE ONE CAN SEE THE CHESTER-PERRY BUILDING......
BOUNCE! BOUNCE! BOUNCE!

WELL, WELL, THIS CROWD OF CHILDREN ARE APPARENTLY ENJOYING THEMSELVES....
GIGGLE! GIGGLE!
THWACK!
OH NO I DIDN'T!
OH YES YOU DID!
GIGGLE!

UPDATED PUNCH AND JUDY? NEVER HEARD OF IT..... LET'S SEE WHAT IT'S ALL ABOUT..
THWACK!
OH NO I DIDN'T!
OH YES YOU DID!
UPDATED PUNCH & JUDY

THWACK!
?
OH, NO I DIDN'T!
OH YES YOU DID!

A LIFE ON THE OCEAN WAVE
SPLOSH! SPLASH! SPLOSH! SPLASH!

FAR OUT ON THE BRINY, JUST DOING MY OWN THING....
WHAT MORE CAN ONE ASK OF A HOLIDAY?

PITY THERE'S NO SUNSHINE TO SPEAK OF BUT IT DOESN'T REALLY MATTER ABOUT THE WEATHER...

IT'S JUST SO GOOD GETTING AWAY FROM THE TREADMILL......
SPLASH! SPLASH! SPLASH! SPLASH!

OH, BOY...THIS IS THE LIFE... MAN AT PEACE WITH THE WORLD...
HOW RELAXING TO SIT HERE GAZING AT A BANK OF FLOWERS....
INSTEAD OF SITTING WITH ONE EYE ON THE CLOCK ALL DAY..........

HELLO THERE—WHY AREN'T YOU WITH THE OTHERS?
I'M FED UP WITH THEM... ALL THEY WANT TO DO IS TALK SHOP AND I CERTAINLY DIDN'T COME ALL THIS WAY TO TALK SHOP.
AND NOW IF YOU WILL EXCUSE ME...

MYSTERY TOUR SIR?
DOFF! DOFF!
WHERE TO?
THAT'S PART OF THE EXCITEMENT, SIR— COULD BE ANYWHERE... YOU DON'T KNOW WHERE YOU ARE TILL YOU ARE THERE...
THINKS:
SOME OTHER TIME!
MUDSEA CARNIVAL
CHESTER-PERRY INDUSTRIES
HOLY MACKEREL.
WILD LIFE
BLOGGS BREWERY
GARDENER
OOOOH!

HOME FROM HOME!

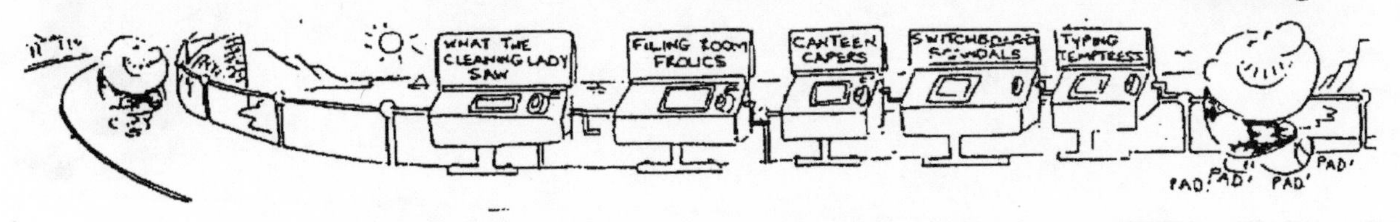

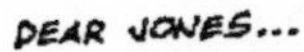

— WEDNESDAY A.M. ...
I EXPECT YOU'LL BE CURSING ME NO END FOR GOING AWAY ON HOLIDAY WITHOUT TELLING YOU THAT **TOP PRIORITY** ORDER NO. 114/D3/2689 IS IN THE BOTTOM LEFT HAND DRAWER IN A FILE MARKED **'MOST URGENT'**

HOPE THIS REACHES YOU IN TIME — BRISTOW.

JUST HAD TO GET THAT OFF MY CONSCIENCE!

I HEAR THE SCRATCHING OF PENS IN THE CHESTER-PERRY BUILDING...

19. BACK TO THE GRINDSTONE

But all good things . . .

I WISH I WAS LIKE FREDDIE 'FRAID O' NO MAN' FINN....
HE DOESN'T WALK TO WORK—HE STRIDES!

WHERE ARE YOU OFF TO IN SUCH A HURRY?
TAKING THE TEA ROUND
BUT MY DEAR – YOUR TROLLEY IS PRACTICALLY EMPTY. YOU'VE LEFT OFF BISCUITS, FAIRY CAKES, SWISS ROLL AND SANDWICHES VARIOUS...
THAT'S RIGHT.... WHO DO YOU THINK I AM – PANSY POTTER THE STRONGMAN'S DAUGHTER?
IF I'D WANTED TO DRIVE A JUGGERNAUT I'D HAVE GOT A JOB AS A JUGGERNAUT DRIVER....

I'VE BEEN LOOKING EVERYWHERE FOR YOU.....
TO TELL YOU THE TRUTH I'M LAYING LOW....
JONES IS READING HIS HOLIDAY DIARY... HE WENT ON A WALKING TOUR....
I NEVER REALISED THE COUNTRY WAS SO BIG....

DESK RAGE...TELEPHONE FURY...FAX FRENZY...MEMO MADNESS...THIS IS ALL NEW TO ME.
I'M SURPRISED TO HEAR THAT... YOU MUST WALK ABOUT WITH YOUR EYES SHUT
THE SYMPTOMS ALWAYS MANIFEST THEMSELVES IN THE SAME WAY....

MARY – PUT ME THROUGH TO GUN & FAMES...
PUTTING YOU THROUGH
CLICK!?
GUN & FAMES?
GOOD MORNING – GUN & FAMES... GET OFF! OFF I SAY!!!
BEG YOUR PARDON?
SORRY ABOUT THAT... CAN I HELP YOU? GET OFF!!!
I SAID GET OFF THIS MINUTE!!
PARDON?
SO SORRY
THE KITTEN IS PLAYING WITH MY BALL OF WOOL....

MORNING, SIR
NEW FACE, EH? WHERE'S MRS. PURDY?
ON HOLIDAY. I'M HER STAND IN....
ARE YOU REALLY? LET ME TASTE YOUR WARE....

IN MY OPINION YOU CAN TELL A LOT ABOUT A TEA LADY BY THE FIRST SIP.....

YUK!!

YOU WERE BORN UNDER THE SIGN OF AQUARIUS, THE WATER CARRIER.......

BUT I CLEARLY ASKED FOR IT TO BE LEFT IN RECEPTION MARKED 'TO BE COLLECTED BY MR. BRISTOW'...
SORRY....
THAT'S DONE IT! I'LL NEVER SEE THAT AGAIN.....
ONCE IT'S FOUND ITS WAY INTO THE SYSTEM....

YOU ARE NOT IN THE MOOD FOR WORK TODAY, MR. BRISTOW?
IMPOSSIBLE....
THE SONGS OF THE NIGHTINGALE ARE PROVING TOO MUCH A DISTRACTION....

WHERE IS EVERYBODY TODAY?
THEY ARE ALL IN THE CLOAKROOM DRYING THEMSELVES DOWN....
LAPFULLS OF HOT TEA?
YOU GOT IT IN ONE.
THEY'VE ONLY THEMSELVES TO BLAME...
THE TEA LADY TAKES HER JOB SERIOUSLY... THE BILLS HAVE TO BE PAID ON TIME....

WELL, MR. MYLES?
WELL, MR. RUDGE?
THIS TIME NEXT YEAR OUR EXTENSION SHOULD BE COMPLETED..
IT CERTAINLY WILL, MR. MYLES —THANKS TO THE BLONDINI BROTHERS...
HARD AT IT STILL.... BRITISH WORKMEN— SALT OF THE EARTH..
DANGER! MEN WORKING OVERHEAD.
MEANWHILE: 500 FEET UP:
Z
Z

GET A MOVE ON, CABBY
SORRY SIR. IT'S IMPOSSIBLE TO MOVE. THE ROAD IS COMPLETELY BLOCKED. I'LL GET OUT AND TAKE A LOOK.
WHAT'S GOING ON?
LISTEN AND YOU'LL FIND OUT.
STONE THE CROWS! I'VE HEARD SOME BAD LANGUAGE DURING MY TWENTY YEARS IN THE NAVY AND MY FIFTEEN YEARS ON THE ROAD. BUT IF THAT DON'T BEAT ALL......
..AND ANOTHER THING. BRISTOW.....

WHAT ON EARTH IS THAT RACKET?
POOR OLD BRISTOW IS ON THE CARPET. HE WAS LATE AGAIN THIS MORNING....
FUDGE IS GOING BERSERK... DO YOU KNOW YOU CAN HEAR HIM FROM THE STREET?
I'M NOT SURPRISED. YOU KNOW WHAT FUDGE IS LIKE WHEN HE GETS THE BIT BETWEEN HIS TEETH.
MEANWHILE: IN A STUDIO AT BROADCASTING HOUSE...
WE INTERRUPT THIS PROGRAMME TO BRING YOU A MOTORING FLASH. DRIVERS ARE WARNED THERE IS VERY HEAVY CONGESTION IN THE ROADS LEADING UP TO AND AROUND THE CHESTER-PERRY BUILDING. MOTORISTS ARE ADVISED TO SEEK ALTERNATIVE ROUTES....

MR BRISTOW — THIS ORDER NUMBER DB 3909....
FORGET IT... YOU'RE WASTING YOUR TIME.
YOU'RE TALKING TO AN EMPTY SUIT.....

WHO'S THAT CHAP THAT ROAMS THE CORRIDORS WITH A PERMANENTLY HAUNTED EXPRESSION?
YOU MUST MEAN THE LEGENDARY RIGBY......
LEGENDARY?
YES...HE CAME THROUGH THE GREAT TEA TROLLEY DISASTER OF '67....
CRIKEY!
MUST BE A HELLUVA SWIMMER!!

HOW ABOUT LUNCH IN THE PARK ?
NOT LIKELY... BEEF STROGONOFF IS ON THE MENU TODAY, AND YOU KNOW HOW I FEEL ABOUT MR. GORDON BLUE'S STROGONOFF....
LUNCH IN THE PARK IS CHEAPER...
BERRIES AND FRUITS OF THE FIELD IT IS......

GROAN! TYPICAL OF UNCLE TED.......
LOOK WHAT I GOT FOR CHRISTMAS....
A 2000 PIECE JIGSAW PUZZLE OF THE CHESTER-PERRY BUILDING...

WON'T YOU WALK A LITTLE FASTER 'STEAD OF CREEPING LIKE A SNAIL..?
THERE'S OLD SOURPUSS CLOSE BEHIND US AND HE'S TREADING ON MY TAIL.....
WILL YOU WON'T YOU, WILL YOU WON'T YOU, SIGN THE LATE LATE BOOK ?

HEAT SEEKING MISSILE

20. HOUSE JOURNALS.

Any strip connected, however vaguely, with House Journals, brings a smile to my lips. I was once invited to give a speech at a function given by the Society of House Journal Editors and accepted with alacrity, since it was to be held at the Criterion in Piccadilly Circus.

Due to circumstances not worth recounting I was unavoidably late and was swiftly ushered to a seat on the top table. The speeches had already started and I became aware that the theme that month was Space. John Glenn's name was bandied about and, realising that House Journal were hot on topicality, I swiftly updated my speech.

My name was requested. (This was no surprise. Editors may be mustard on Space but sadly lacking on social etiquette!) I told them and when called to stand, made a freewheeling speech in which I mentioned Neil Armstrong and every other astronaut I could put name to, tying them in rather neatly with House Journals and Bristow's attitude. (The reason for the invite.) I sat down to a polite clapping. This was frankly, not what I expected, and to cover my embarrassment I picked up the menu card.

'Which unit are you from?' the neighbour on my right asked, choosing his words carefully.

'I'm not from a unit.' I smiled. 'I'm with the **Evening Standard***.'*

Then I felt a chill run down my spine.

Across the top of the menu the heading read 'Space and Aviation Society of Great Britain'.

The House Journal Editor's Dinner was on the floor above.

Whoops!

IN ALL MY YEARS AS A MARRIAGE COUNSELLOR I HAVE NEVER EXPERIENCED THIS SITUATION...
BECAUSE OF YOUR TOTAL OBSESSION WITH YOUR COMPANY'S HOUSE JOURNAL YOU ARE QUITE PREPARED TO SEE YOUR MARRIAGE GO DOWN THE DRAIN?
THAT'S RIGHT...
WHAT ABOUT THE CHILDREN?
SHE CAN KEEP THE KIDS...

ARE YOU SAYING THE COMPANY HOUSE JOURNAL WAS RESPONSIBLE FOR THE BREAK UP OF YOUR MARRIAGE?
I NEVER CALLED IT A HOUSE JOURNAL...
WHEN I DIE YOU WILL FIND THE WORDS 'NEWSLETTER' ENGRAVED ON MY HEART.....

EDITING THE COMPANY HOUSE JOURNAL IS DRIVING ME CRAZY....
MY LIFE IS RUINED AND MY MARRIAGE ON THE ROCKS...
IS WHAT I'M DOING WORTH IT?
NO.

YOU ARE SAYING THAT YOUR MARRIAGE HAS SUFFERED BECAUSE YOUR HUSBAND SPENDS TOO MUCH TIME WORKING ON HIS COMPANY'S HOUSE JOURNAL?
NOT JUST SUFFERED... IT'S OVER, FINITO, CAPUT...
HE COMES HOME EVERY NIGHT SMELLING OF DRINK, LIPSTICK ON HIS COLLAR....

HERE IT IS, BRISTOW – THE BUMPER SPRING NUMBER OF THE CHESTER-PERRY HOUSE JOURNAL...
NO THANKS...
NO THANKS? YOU CAN'T SAY 'NO THANKS'... YOU CAN TAKE IT AND DISPOSE OF IT BUT YOU CAN'T SAY 'NO THANKS'...
NOBODY HAS EVER SAID NO THANKS... HOW CAN ANYBODY SAY NO THANKS..?
SEND DOWN THE MEN IN WHITE COATS....

21. STRANGERS IN THE HOUSE.

Tillie's Temps, (Suppliers of Typists to the Needy) seem to be a magnet for single girls who have no apparent desire in life other than land a husband.

The Chester-Perry Organisation, thanks to the soft hearted Mr Perkins of Personnel, are forever engaging these young ladies who seem confused the moment they see an office and are prone to the vapours when seated at a word processor.

Bristow is wise to these feminine stratagems, and gives no quarter. Temps who arrive at the Chester-Perry building in 'pristine condition' are reputed to arrive back at the bureau as 'battle-scared war veterans'.

It is not hard to understand why.

There are other organisations who supply a different type of girl. Trendi-Temps, for example, have girls with 'lived in faces'.

TEMPestuous supplies girls of the ilk . . .

While of TEMPtation there is little to say . . .

Bristow is not 'phased' by any of these, of course, but carries on being insufferable.

22. LIVING DEATH IN THE BUYING DEPARTMENT...

Bristow started work on his opus **Living Death in the Buying Department** (an **exposé** of office life) twenty-two years ago and has never stopped updating and revising it.

At the time of going to press it is once again in the hands of Messrs Heap and Trottwood (Publishers to the Prols), who have never stopped rejecting this or any other of his literary efforts.

INCREDIBLE — MESSRS. HEAP AND TROTTWOOD, (PUBLISHERS TO THE PROLES) HAVE SENT BACK THE MANUSCRIPT OF MY BOOK 'LIVING DEATH IN THE BUYING DEPARTMENT' BY RETURN OF POST!!

THIS IMPLIES A SLAP ACROSS THE FACE! THEY SIMPLY DON'T WANT TO KNOW!!

IT'S TRAGIC TO THINK THAT FOR ME, AS AN AUTHOR, THE WRITING IS ON THE WALL.....

WOULD YOU BELIEVE IT — THOSE DAMNED PUBLISHERS, HEAP & TROTWOOD, HAVE REJECTED MY LATEST MANUSCRIPT....
LISTEN TO THIS.....
DEAR SIR, WE ARE RETURNING HEREWITH YOUR UNTITLED MANUSCRIPT CONCERNING THE BUYING CLERK WHO FELL ASLEEP AT HIS DESK FOR FORTY YEARS.... WHILST WE APPRECIATE YOUR SUBMITTING IT TO US WE REGRETFULLY POINT OUT THAT WE DO NOT ANTICIPATE A GREAT DEMAND FOR A WORK OF THIS IMPROBABLE NATURE.. YOURS FAITHFULLY ETC, ETC..

RIDICULOUS! WHAT'S SO IMPROBABLE ABOUT A BUYING CLERK WHO FALLS ASLEEP FOR FORTY YEARS?

AH, WELL — BACK TO THE DRAWING BOARD..

Bristow is not alone in striving to make a fast buck. Other members of the staff are also keen to make a few shillings on the side by writing a best seller.

MORNING LADIES...I WONDER WHETHER YOU CAN HELP...?
I'VE WRITTEN A BOOK ENTITLED 'LIVING DEATH IN THE BUYING DEPARTMENT' AND I WONDER WHETHER ANY OF YOU COULD TYPE IT OUT FOR ME?
NOT TILL I'VE FINISHED 'LIVING DEATH IN THE POST ROOM' BY MR. KNIGHT.....
NOT TILL I'VE FINISHED 'LIVING DEATH IN GOODS INWARD' BY MR. FROST...
NOT TILL I'VE FINISHED 'LIVING DEATH IN THE ACCOUNTS' BY MR. HOUGHTON...
NOT TILL I'VE FINISHED 'LIVING DEATH IN PRODUCTION CONTROL' BY MR. MOULAND...

MR. PERKINS– WHAT A COINCIDENCE! TO THINK I'VE BEEN SECRETLY WORKING ON MY BOOK 'LIVING DEATH IN THE BUYING DEPARTMENT' AND JUST A FEW YARDS AWAY YOU'VE BEEN ENGAGED ON A SIMILAR PROJECT...
IT'S A SMALL WORLD AND NO MISTAKE..
SPEAKING AS ONE WRITER TO ANOTHER, HOW LONG DID IT TAKE YOU TO WRITE 'LIVING DEATH IN PERSONNEL'?
SIX YEARS TO THE DAY—AND YOU
SIX YEARS TO THE DAY..
AMAZING! YOU WORK WEEKENDS AND EVENINGS, I SUPPOSE?
NOT LIKELY- DO YOU?
NOT LIKELY...
I START AT NINE IN THE MORNING AND FINISH AT FIVE...
MY OWN STORY EXACTLY.

MR. BRISTOW — THIS BOOK 'LIVING DEATH IN THE BUYING DEPARTMENT' IS DYNAMITE!!!!
IMPACT! MISS SUNMAN... IMPACT! HIT 'EM! KICK 'EM! SOCK 'EM! GIVE THEM THE OLD WHAMMEE! LET'S SEE HEADS ROLL!!
YOU WON'T TELL THEM WHO TYPED IT OUT, WILL YOU?

BRISTOW — HOW ON EARTH DID YOU MANAGE TO FIND THE TIME TO WRITE A BOOK OF THIS LENGTH?
I DON'T KNOW, REALLY.....
I JUST PICKED IT UP WHENEVER I HAD A SPARE MINUTE.......

THIS 948 PAGE MANUSCRIPT OF YOURS WILL CERTAINLY RAISE A FEW EYEBROWS.....
YOU MEAN LIKE WHERE DID HE GET THE INFO? WHERE DID HE GET THE LOW DOWN?
NO.....
WHERE DID HE GET THE PAPER? WHERE DID HE FIND THE TIME......?
'MORNING, MR. BRISTOW...
'MORNING MR. PERKINS...
WHAT'S THAT YOU'VE GOT THERE?
IT'S THE MANUSCRIPT OF MY AS YET UNPUBLISHED NOVEL... 'LIVING DEATH IN THE BUYING DEPARTMENT' AN EXPOSÉ OF BIG BUSINESS...
IT'S THE MANUSCRIPT OF MY AS YET UNPUBLISHED NOVEL 'LIVING DEATH IN PERSONNEL' AN EXPOSÉ OF BIG BUSINESS....
WHAT A SURPRISE— I DIDN'T KNOW YOU WERE A WRITER...
HOW EXTRAORDINARY. US BEING ON THE SAME WAVELENGTH— AM I MENTIONED IN YOUR BOOK?
YES— ON PAGES 41, 67, 92, 147, 253–

23. BUT SERIOUSLY...

The hardest thing about putting this book together was not deciding which strips to put in, but which to leave out. When one is faced with ten thousand of these and needs but two hundred to put over the 'flavour' of the strip to someone who has never heard of or seen it, is not easy, for there have been major changes in the world of business. These changes have naturally had some bearing on the selection of strips, for the new reader may not be familiar with the quill pen and gaslight world in which Bristow describes his early days. (Not that too much credibility should be attached to these, for in one telling episode he is overheard telling the Post Boy he was apprenticed to a Victorian chimney sweep!) We have therefore, and this is where the hard part comes in, pruned drastically the episodes that are light years away from Modern Times and zoomed in on those of the present.

We are, not to mince matters, sucking up to Youth, for over the years technology has introduced itself, and it's the kids that are in the driving seat. When Bristow started with the Chester-Perry Organisation in 1960 typewriters and carbon paper were considered the bees knees. Wage packets containing notes and coins were handed out on Fridays. Telephones had dials and your fingers really did the walking. Fountain pens were the rage, bowler hats were doffed and pin striped trousers were still fashionable. A trifle sadly (except for the Chester-Perry Company, it seems), apart from the fountain pens, these things are no longer with us, and progress marches on triumphantly. Since the strip began, the social scene has also changed, and, because of this, characters that appeared in the early days have passed into obscurity.

In the seventies, for example, when Traffic Wardens first appeared on the streets, I introduced Warden 262, who strictly enforced the parking regulations of that time. 'My views on everything and anything are exactly the same as those expressed by the Ministry of Transport, whichever party is in power,' she would say, with pride in her voice. (I stopped using her when a real life warden who did not share my sense of humour discovered my identity and waged a one-woman campaign against me.) Now, alas, traffic wardens are commonplace, their novelty having worn off, and 262 walks off into the sunset, pausing only to check a meter or two . . .

24. BUY! BUY! BUY!

In the late sixties a rather interesting thing happened, for Bristow was suddenly involved in advertising.

It was the result of a strip in which Bristow was portrayed hurrying to work carrying a rather bulky briefcase. This was obviously slowing him down. He decided therefore to jettison some of the sandwiches he was carrying.

My lack of drawing ability meant that the action lacked the impact I was after and seeking to remedy this I added the words 'jettison! jettison!'

Without realising it I had stumbled on something that was of interest to advertising agencies, for within days I was besieged by offers of work.

They could describe their product by putting in descriptive words – gleam! gleam! glitter! glitter! This was new at the time and I was only too happy to oblige.

25. KILLING TIME.

POSTCARD FROM MISS SUNMAN OF THE TYPING POOL....

'HAVING A WONDERFUL TIME IN THIS FAIRY TALE VILLAGE. EVERYONE HERE IS EXTREMELY FRIENDLY.

YESTERDAY I HAD MY BOTTOM PINCHED BY A LONELY GOATHERD....'

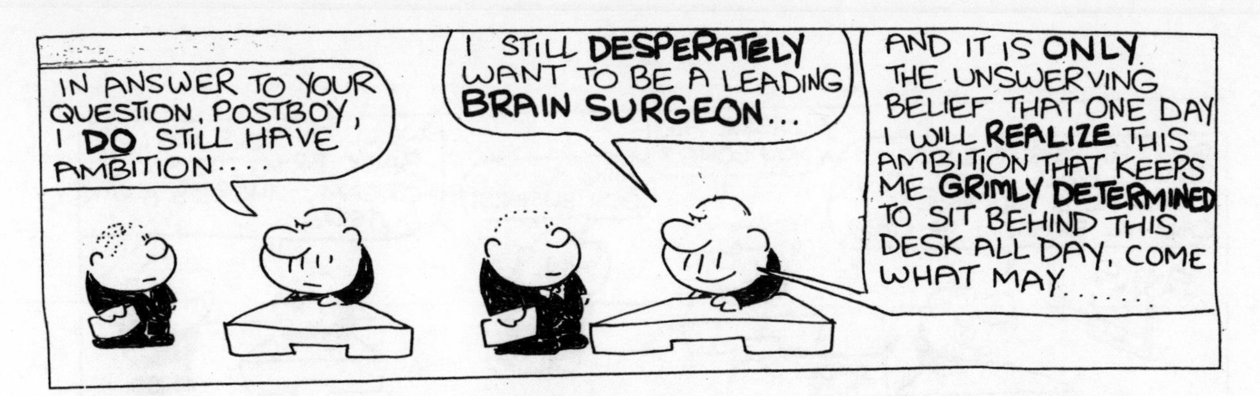

ISN'T IT **MARVELLOUS**?

EVERY SINGLE ACTION, MAN MADE OR OTHERWISE, NEAR OR FAR ON THE FACE OF THE EARTH, HITS ME IN THE POCKET....

GOOD HEAVENS! A SUDDEN PEAL OF BELLS —— AND IT SOUNDS AS IF THEY ARE CALLING 'BRISTOW...BRISTOW'
SHADES OF DICK WHITTINGTON!
WHERE ARE YOU GOING?
MIND YOUR OWN BUSINESS
WELL, ON YOUR WAY BACK BRING ME AN ICE CREAM... THERE'S A VAN OUTSIDE.....

EIGHT O'CLOCK SHAVE....
FOLLOWED BY
NINE O'CLOCK SHADOW.....

WELL, WELL, WELL, SO YOU WORK FOR THE CHESTER-PERRY ORGANISATION......
RELAXED THEIR STANDARDS THAT MUCH, HAVE THEY?

IT'S ONE OF THOSE DAYS WHEN EVERYTHING GOES RIGHT... STAND ASIDE JONES — ANY PLACE I HANG MY HAT IS HOME...
IT LANDED IN THE GUTTER
SOB!

WELL, WELL — SIR REGINALD CHESTER-PERRY'S ROLLS ROYCE...

WHAT ARE YOU DOING IN THIS NECK OF THE WOODS?
SIR REGINALD IS LEAVING ON HIS ANNUAL WINTER CRUISE TODAY.— I'M TAKING HIM TO THE AIRPORT TO CATCH HIS PRIVATE PLANE TO SOUTHAMPTON WHERE HIS YACHT IS WAITING....

I SEE — ROLLS TO THE AIRPORT, PRIVATE PLANE TO SOUTHAMPTON AND FROM THERE, LUXURY YACHT TO THE SUN...
I'M GLAD YOU TOLD ME THAT....

IT'S CHEERED-UP WHAT WOULD OTHERWISE HAVE BEEN A MOST DEPRESSING MONDAY MORNING!

SIR REGINALD CHESTER-PERRY'S ROLLS ROYCE IS OUTSIDE...
SIGH!
ANOTHER CUP TO WASH UP...
SEEN TODAY'S 'DAILY THINGS'? OUR DIRECTORS HAVE COMMISSIONED AN OIL PAINTING OF SIR REGINALD TO HANG IN THE BOARDROOM.....
SIGH! SOMETHING ELSE TO DUST...............

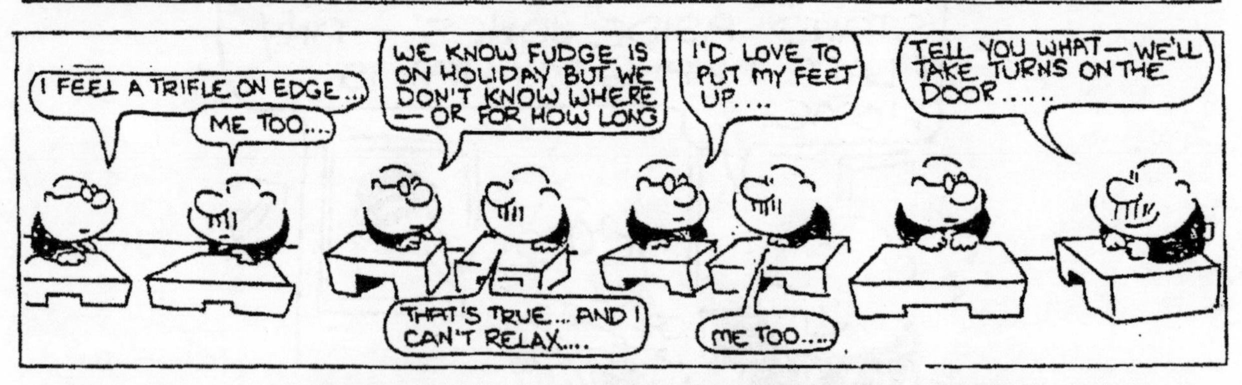

I FEEL A TRIFLE ON EDGE...
ME TOO....
WE KNOW FUDGE IS ON HOLIDAY BUT WE DON'T KNOW WHERE — OR FOR HOW LONG
THAT'S TRUE... AND I CAN'T RELAX....
I'D LOVE TO PUT MY FEET UP....
ME TOO....
TELL YOU WHAT — WE'LL TAKE TURNS ON THE DOOR......

CHEER UP, MR. DIMKINS
CHEER UP, HE SAYS! I FEEL LIKE SCREAMING AT THE TOP OF MY VOICE...
I DON'T KNOW WHETHER YOU EXPERIENCE THIS, BRISTOW, BUT I FIND THERE IS ONE HOUR DURING THE DAY WHEN THE CLOCK SEEMS TO STAND ABSOLUTELY STILL...
ONE HOUR???

BOP!
OUCH!!!
STAGGER! STAGGER!

I'VE BEEN USING MY 'BUTTER-WOULDN'T-MELT-IN-MY-MOUTH' EXPRESSION AGAIN... AND AGAIN IT HASN'T COME OFF...

THINK I'LL CALL IT A DAY AS FAR AS THAT EXPRESSION IS CONCERNED...

MY FEATURES ARE GETTING THAT BATTERED IT'S HARD TO TELL WHEN I'M USING IT ANYWAY...

MMH! THE CLEANING LADIES HAVE BEEN UP TO THEIR TRICKS AGAIN...
OH?
SIGNS ARE A NEW CLEANER STARTED THIS MORNING AND THEY GAVE HER MY DESK AND SURROUNDS TO GET ON WITH...
SHE STARTED OFF WITH PLENTY OF ELBOW GREASE BUT FINALLY THE JOB GOT ON TOP OF HER AND SHE CRACKED UP...
HOW ON EARTH—?
STANDS OUT A MILE... COME OVER HERE AND LOOK AT THIS...
NOTICE THE WAY THE TEARDROPS COAGULATE IN THE DUST....

WHAT DO YOU PEOPLE AT GUN & FAMES TAKE ME FOR —AN IDIOT?
SWIMMING POOLS AND POLO PONIES, MY FOOT! I WASN'T BORN YESTERDAY...
NOW THEN, ABOUT THIS ORDER—
SORRY, MR. BRISTOW... MIND IF I HANG UP? THE WAGES ARE COMING ROUND AND I SHALL NEED BOTH HANDS...
SOB!
HELLO? HELLO? HELLO?

WHAT IS SECURITY LIKE AT YOUR FIRM?
STRICT...
DO THEY SEARCH YOU AS YOU LEAVE?
NO
WE GET SEARCHED AS WE ARRIVE.....

I'VE BEEN WATCHING YOU FOR HALF AN HOUR AND YOU HAVEN'T MOVED....
FOR THE MONEY I GET HERE I SHOULD PLAY WITH A FULL DECK....?

WAITING FOR ME?
IF YOUR NAME IS CHESTER-PERRY, YES!
CP 1
LOVELY CAR
HE'S GETTING A NEW ONE TOMORROW!
CP 1
WHAT'S HE GOING TO DO WITH THIS ONE—TRADE IT IN?
NO. ABANDON IT IN SOME BACK ALLEY!
CP 1

BUT SURELY PROMOTION COMES EASY IF ONE HAS THE ABILITY?
NO, NO, NO...
ABILITY COUNTS FOR VERY LITTLE HERE...
PROMOTION COMES ALPHABETICALLY, OR WITH AGE.....

THE TROUBLE WITH HAVING LUNCH IN THE PARK WITH YOU, JONES, IS THAT YOU TURN IT INTO A MAJOR PRODUCTION.....
NONSENSE!!
I'VE TAKEN THE LIBERTY OF BRINGING TWO CANS OF INSECT REPELLENT...
YOU TAKE THE WAR MEMORIAL TO THE BOATING LAKE AND I'LL DO THE BANDSTAND DOWN TO THE CRAZY GOLF......

ARE YOU TELLING ME THAT SHIRLEY DIMPLE WAS ASKING AFTER ME WHILE I WAS ON HOLIDAY?
YES, BUT I SHOULDN'T READ TOO MUCH INTO THAT, IF I WERE YOU. SHE'S OBVIOUSLY AS NUTTY AS A FRUITCAKE....
UNLIKE THE REST OF US, WHO SEE YOU AS AN OBJECT OF DERISION, SHE APPARENTLY SEES SOMETHING WORTHWILE.....

FINISHED WITH YOUR CUP DEAR?
YES THANK YOU
WHAT'S WRONG WITH YOUR TEA?
TASTE IT — THAT'S WHAT'S WRONG WITH IT.

WHAT A SHAME! YOUR CAKE HAS FALLEN ONTO THE GROUND.
FALL NOTHING — IT WAS PUSHED!

I HAPPENED TO BE GOING THROUGH THE FILES AND CAME ACROSS THIS FADED LETTER.... IT'S ADDRESSED TO CONVICT NUMBER 316262..!!

3126262 EH? THAT TAKES ME BACK... HE WAS AN OLD PEN FRIEND.....

WHEN I JOINED THE FIRM, CHESTER-PERRY'S WAS TWINNED WITH DEVIL'S ISLAND......

MR. BRISTOW — YOU DIDN'T REALLY HAVE A PEN FRIEND ON DEVIL'S ISLAND?
POOR EMIL.... CONVICT NUMBER 3126262.... ....
THEY WORKED HIM TO DEATH, Y'KNOW.......
KEPT SENDING HIM BIGGER AND BIGGER IN-TRAYS.....

FUDGE WANTS YOU IN HIS OFFICE
GOSH!

IT'S SO LONG SINCE HE CALLED ME INTO HIS OFFICE I'VE FORGOTTEN HOW TO ARRANGE MY FEATURES......

BOY, OH BOY — AM I GLAD THAT'S OVER...
SLAM!
LONG DAY?
NO..... USUAL EIGHT HOURS.
NINE FIFTEEN TILL QUARTER TO FIVE........

WHY IS BRISTOW LOOKING SO SOULFUL ALL OF A SUDDEN...?
HAVEN'T YOU HEARD?
IT'S 'HAVE A BUYING CLERK IN YOUR HOME' WEEK....

GOOD MORNING!
GOOD MORNING...
ALLOW ME TO INTRODUCE MYSELF.....MY NAME IS THUSE...JOHN THUSE....
I STARTED WORK WITH THE COMPANY THIS MORNING AND I WANT TO GET THE FEEL OF THE PLACE....
TO KNOW WHO IS WHO AND HOW THEY FIT INTO THE SCHEME OF THINGS....
I THOUGHT I'D START WITH THE BUYING DEPARTMENT...
GOOD THINKING
MY NAME IS THIRKETTLE AND I'D LIKE TO OFFER YOU EVERY ASSISTANCE...

LOOK AT THE TIME — 8.35 AND NO SIGN OF THE 8.15 COMMUTER SPECIAL....
DAMN! I MUSTN'T BE LATE TODAY WHATEVER HAPPENS...
A PLAGUE ON BRITISH HI-SPEED RAIL... AWARDING THEIR EMPLOYEES SUCH A MASSIVE PAY RISE....
THEY'RE SO WELL PAID THEY COULDN'T CARE LESS ABOUT US PASSENGERS...
TELL YOU WHAT... WHY DON'T THE FOUR OF US SHARE A CAB...?
GOOD IDEA — COME ON!!
TAXIS RESERVED FOR STATION STAFF ONLY

WHERE'S MR. GORDON BLUE, THE CHEF?
HE'S OVER THERE INSPECTING THE COOKING SHERRY...
MR. BLUE — DISASTER! THE PROVISIONS HAVEN'T ARRIVED, THE GROCER HAS LET US DOWN AGAIN...
SO.... NO PROVISIONS AND FIVE HUNDRED PEOPLE TO FEED...
WHAT'S TO BE DONE?
BRING ME TWO LOAVES AND FIVE FISHES....

WELL GENTLEMEN — WHAT'S IT TO BE?
WHO KNOWS? THE STATE THESE MENU CARDS ARE IN!
THEY ARE INDECIPHERABLE...
TELL YOU WHAT LET'S PLAY POT LUCK.
I'LL HAVE WHATEVER'S WRITTEN UNDER THIS BLOB OF CUSTARD..
I'LL TAKE WHATEVER'S WRITTEN UNDER THIS TOMATO KETCHUP
I'LL TAKE THE GRAVY STAIN
BAGS I THE GREASY THUMBPRINT...

MR. GORDON BLUE — A WORD WITH YOU...
IF IT IS ABOUT TODAYS LUNCH I CAN EXPLAIN EVERYTHING.... THERE WAS A POWER CUT- THE FRIDGE BROKE DOWN. THE OVEN —
IT'S ABOUT THE STATE OF THE MENU CARDS. THEY ARE SO STAINED IT IS DISGUSTING. EVEN YOUR MOST HARDENED CUSTOMERS ARE COMPLAINING. I HAVE HERE A PETITION SIGNED BY ALL YOUR REGULARS..
BUT I CANNOT READ A WORD..
SORRY ABOUT THAT- —LEAKY PEN!

HOW MUCH DID YOU COLLECT FOR MR. MAGGS' RETIREMENT PRESENT?
A GRAND TOTAL OF £125......
£125 FOR 50 YEARS WORK, EH?
5 DAY WEEK.... LESS HOLIDAYS FOR 50 YEARS... 'CETRA... 'CETRA...
BEARS OUT THE OLD CHESTER-PERRY MAXIM....
HE SHALL HAVE BUT A PENNY A DAY......
COME ALONG, DUANE DEAR —YOU DON'T WANT TO BE LATE ON YOUR FIRST DAY AT WORK, DO YOU?
I DON'T WANT TO GO TO WORK!
DON'T LET'S GO THROUGH ALL THAT AGAIN... YOU'RE GOING TO WORK AND THAT'S IT!
BUT MUM —!
THAT'S ENOUGH....
I DON'T WANT TO GO TO WORK IN THE NASTY HORRIBLE ROTTEN CHESTER-PERRY BUILDING
YOU AND ME BOTH, KID......

DON'T TELL ME YOU'RE STILL THINKING ABOUT THE ROAD WIDENING SCHEME CUTTING INTO THE PARK?
TO TELL YOU THE TRUTH I'M THINKING ABOUT THE TRAMP THAT STROLLS AROUND THERE ALL DAY....
IF THEY CARRY ON CUTTING INTO THE PARK, THE POOR DEVIL WILL FIND HIMSELF WALKING THE STREETS...

IN MY OPINION MR. JONES WAS WRONG TO GO ON HOLIDAY AT THE PRESENT TIME.....
THINGS ARE CHANGING SO FAST IT'S DIFFICULT TO STAY AHEAD OF THE GAME EVEN IF YOU ARE IN THE BUILDING....
SOMETIMES I GET BACK FROM LUNCH AND FIND MYSELF WOEFULLY OUT OF TOUCH.....

ALL THOSE AGAINST?
SPORTS & SOCIAL CLUB
PRETTY DECISIVE...
THE PROPOSAL THAT WE HOLD THE MILLENIUM CELEBRATIONS IN THE BROOM CUPBOARD IS DEFEATED...

MR. BRISTOW?
GOOD HEAVENS, NO! HE'S PROBABLY OUT IN THE CORRIDOR...
YOU'LL RECOGNISE HIM AS SOON AS YOU SET EYES ON HIM...
HE WALKS AROUND THE BUILDING LIKE A RURAL POSTMAN.....

BRISTOW — IT'S THE REAL THING...
EVERY TIME I HEAR THE CLATTERING OF HER TYPEWRITER I GET PRICKLES RUNNING UP AND DOWN MY SPINE......

ARE YOU SERIOUSLY TELLING ME THAT YOU AND THE GORGEOUS MISS PRETTY OF KLEENAPHONE HAVE GOT IT TOGETHER?
POST BOY
YOU KNOW HOW THESE RUMOURS GET AROUND.....
THERE IS ALWAYS A VIOLENT CHEMICAL REACTION WHEN SHE STANDS ANYWHERE NEAR ME, I CAN TELL YOU....
SOME SAY IT'S THE SMELL OF HER DISINFECTANT AND MY AFTER-SHAVE COMING TOGETHER BUT PERSONALLY.....

DID YOU SEE THE NEW YEAR IN?
I'M AFRAID SO — IT WAS LIKE A HORRIBLE DREAM....
AS THE FIRST NOTE OF MIDNIGHT RANG OUT MOST OF US, REALISING WE HAD ANOTHER YEAR OF THE SAME TO GET THROUGH, CLUNG TO EACH OTHER FOR SUPPORT......

HAVE YOU BEEN KEEPING JONES'S WORK UP TO DATE WHILE HE'S BEEN ON HOLIDAY?
NO — I'M LEAVING IT UNTIL HE ACTUALLY RE ENTERS THE BUILDING...
STRANGE, REALLY... I FIND I DO MY BEST WORK WHEN I LEAVE THINGS TILL THE LAST MINUTE AND THEN GO FOR IT LIKE A BULL AT A GATE....
STRANGE INDEED...

Scene: The head office of Messrs Heap and Trottwood, Publishers of Fine Works...
'MORNING, MR TASKER – NICE WEEKEND?
DON'T ASK... LOOK WHAT THEY GAVE ME TO READ: "THE FINISH OF THE FAT MAN"
DON'T TELL ME — A LACONIC GUN-TOTING PRIVATE EYE STORY... A BLONDE ON EVERY PAGE AND A SYDNEY GREENSTREET TYPE BADDIE....
NO SUCH LUCK..
IT'S ABOUT THIS BUYING CLERK WHO GOES ON A CRASH DIET.........
GROAN!

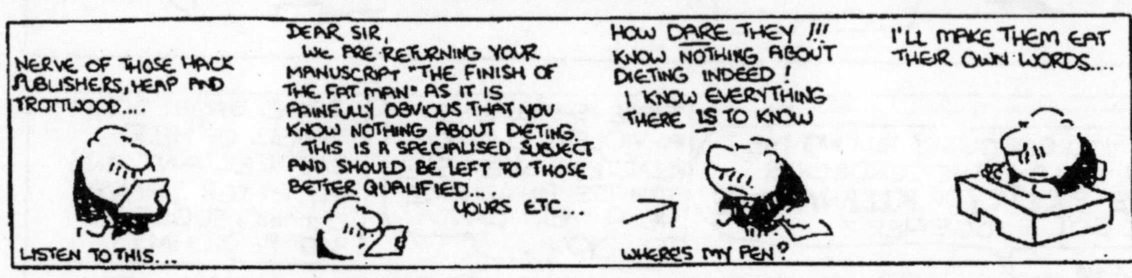

NERVE OF THOSE HACK PUBLISHERS, HEAP AND TROTTWOOD....
LISTEN TO THIS...
DEAR SIR, WE ARE RETURNING YOUR MANUSCRIPT "THE FINISH OF THE FAT MAN" AS IT IS PAINFULLY OBVIOUS THAT YOU KNOW NOTHING ABOUT DIETING. THIS IS A SPECIALISED SUBJECT AND SHOULD BE LEFT TO THOSE BETTER QUALIFIED... YOURS ETC...
HOW DARE THEY !!! KNOW NOTHING ABOUT DIETING INDEED! I KNOW EVERYTHING THERE IS TO KNOW
WHERE'S MY PEN?
I'LL MAKE THEM EAT THEIR OWN WORDS...

WHAT'S SIR REGINALD CHESTER-FERRY LIKE? WHAT KIND OF MAN IS OUR BELOVED FIRM'S FOUNDER?
SIR REGINALD? GOD BLESS HIM! THE FINEST BOSS A MAN EVER HAD....
IS HE AS STERN AND UNYIELDING AS THEY MAKE HIM OUT TO BE?
NO. COMPLETE OPPOSITE... CHARMING FELLOW...
I'VE SEEN HIM ON THE BOX A FEW TIMES BUT I'VE NEVER SEEN HIM SMILE. DOES HE HAVE A SENSE OF HUMOUR?
MARVELLOUS SENSE OF HUMOUR..
YOU SHOULD JUST HEAR HIM LAUGHING IN BED AROUND NINE O'CLOCK ON A RAINY MONDAY MORNING.........

I'VE GOT TO HAND IT TO YOU, BRISTOW – YOU WERE MAGNIFICENT...
I'VE NEVER HEARD FUDGE GIVING ANYONE SUCH A DRESSING DOWN IN PUBLIC...
WAVE UPON WAVE OF INVECTIVE DELIVERED AT THE TOP OF HIS VOICE AND YOU DIDN'T BAT AN EYELID....
YOU STOOD THERE WITH YOUR EYES LOWERED AND YOUR FISTS LIGHTLY CLENCHED, TOTALLY OBLIVIOUS TO ANYTHING HE MIGHT HAVE SAID... HOW DID YOU DO IT?
EASY PEASY..
I GOT THE IDEA FROM SOMEONE I ONCE SAW OPERATING A PNEUMATIC DRILL.......

YOU SAID YOU WERE GOING TO WORK HARD TODAY...
I AM WORKING AS HARD AS I CAN....
I'VE ONLY ONE OAR IN THE WATER...

ARE THEY REALLY TELEVISING THE QUARTER FINALS OF THE DESK-TOP FOOTBALL CHAMPIONSHIPS NEXT WEEK?
NEVER HEARD OF IT.....
YES.. ON THE NEW WHITE COLLAR CHANNEL....
YOU WOULDN'T.... IT GOES OUT AT NINE AND FINISHES AT FIVE ...

BRISTOW — I AM EDITOR OF THE HOUSE JOURNAL YOU HAVE CONSIGNED TO THE WASTEPAPER BASKET...
OF COURSE I AM HURT...
I AM ONLY HUMAN AND HATE TO SEE THE FRUITS OF MY LABOUR CONDEMNED TO A WASTEPAPER BASKET... CAN'T YOU SEE THAT?
NO, NOT REALLY...

I'LL HAVE YOU KNOW, JONES, THAT MY THREATENING LETTERS ARE VERY CAREFULLY WRITTEN....
WHEN I MISPLACE A WORD I HAVE SOMETIMES TO CHANGE EIGHT OR NINE PAGES....

JONES— I'D LIKE YOUR HONEST OPINION....
FIRE AWAY.
MY TELEPHONE VOICE... GOOD OR BAD?
YOUR TELEPHONE SPEAKING VOICE?
LET'S SEE—HOW DOES SHAKESPEARE PUT IT— 'SHALL I COMPARE THEE TO A SQUEAKY GATE?'

THE NEXT OFFICE ON THE RIGHT IS THE BUYING DEPARTMENT. WOULD YOU LIKE TO SEE HOW THEY OPERATE?
WELL, IT'S NOT ON MY ITINERY BUT I'LL CALL IN AND SAY HELLO...
Z
Z
OH, DEAR—TOO LATE... THE SANDMAN'S BEEN

The above is one of a batch of five that ran into difficulties with the Unions in the sixties.

A reader wrote to me complaining about a spelling mistake and not wishing to repeat this I decided to have the strips checked by a Proof Reader. (They check all copy before it is published.)

They are members of a Union.

Before I go any further let me explain that Bristow was being sold by the **Evening Standard** *to other newspapers. This practice is called Syndication. I duly presented the batch of strips to one of the Readers.*

He looked at the pieces of artwork and raised his eyebrows expectantly.

'If you could just read them for spelling mistakes,' I ventured.

'I read for the **Standard** today,' he replied. 'Are these for the **Standard**?'

'These go into the **Standard** eventually,' I said brightly. 'After Syndication,' I added, foolishly.

'I read for Syndication on Thursdays,' he said, returning them. 'Bring them back on Thursday.'

'If you could read them now,' I smiled. 'It would save me a lot of bother.'

'You said they go to Syndication first,' he said patiently. 'I read for Syndication Thursdays. Are you deaf?'

'But they go into the **Standard** EVENTUALLY,' I explained. 'You don't need to read them twice – or do you?' I added hastily, for a look that was a mixture of hardness and strangeness had crossed his face.

'You mean you read them TWICE?' I went on.

'I read them for Syndication and I read them for the **Standard**,' he said doggedly, reaching for the phone.

They were 'blacked'. This time for a whole week.

'Don't keep causing trouble,' I was told by someone Pretty High Up in Management.

Those were the days.

26. PAY DAY...

A few years ago I had a gag that involved drawing the Chester-Perry building. This takes a lot of time, and the deadline was fast approaching. I suddenly remembered having once been in the office when the lads were opening their wages (or wage remittances!) and noting that the inside of the envelopes carried a pattern not unlike that of the Chester-Perry building.

Chuckling the while, I obtained two of these envelopes, opened them and stuck them down. You can see the result in the strip below. I was well pleased and resolved there and then to use pay packets every time I needed a Chester-Perry building.

A reader, who I had never met, but who took it upon himself to telephone me every now and then with words of encouragement ('Thin on the ground, this week, Mr Dickens?' or worse, 'Running out of ideas, are we?') rang me on the day this appeared.

'I won't ring you any more, Frank,' he said. 'I see by today's strip we earn the same money.'

Cheek!

WHY DO I WORK HERE?
I WAS JOB HUNTING AND SAW THIS BUILDING OUT OF THE CORNER OF MY EYE...

HOW COME I'M ALWAYS IN THE DOG HOUSE? I MEAN, IF EVER THERE WAS A COMPANY MAN, I'M IT!

IF I SHOULD QUIT, THINK ONLY THIS OF ME: THAT THERE'S SOME CORNER OF A FOREIGN FIRM THAT IS FOREVER CHESTER-PERRYS...

27. MEANWHILE, BACK IN THE OFFICE....

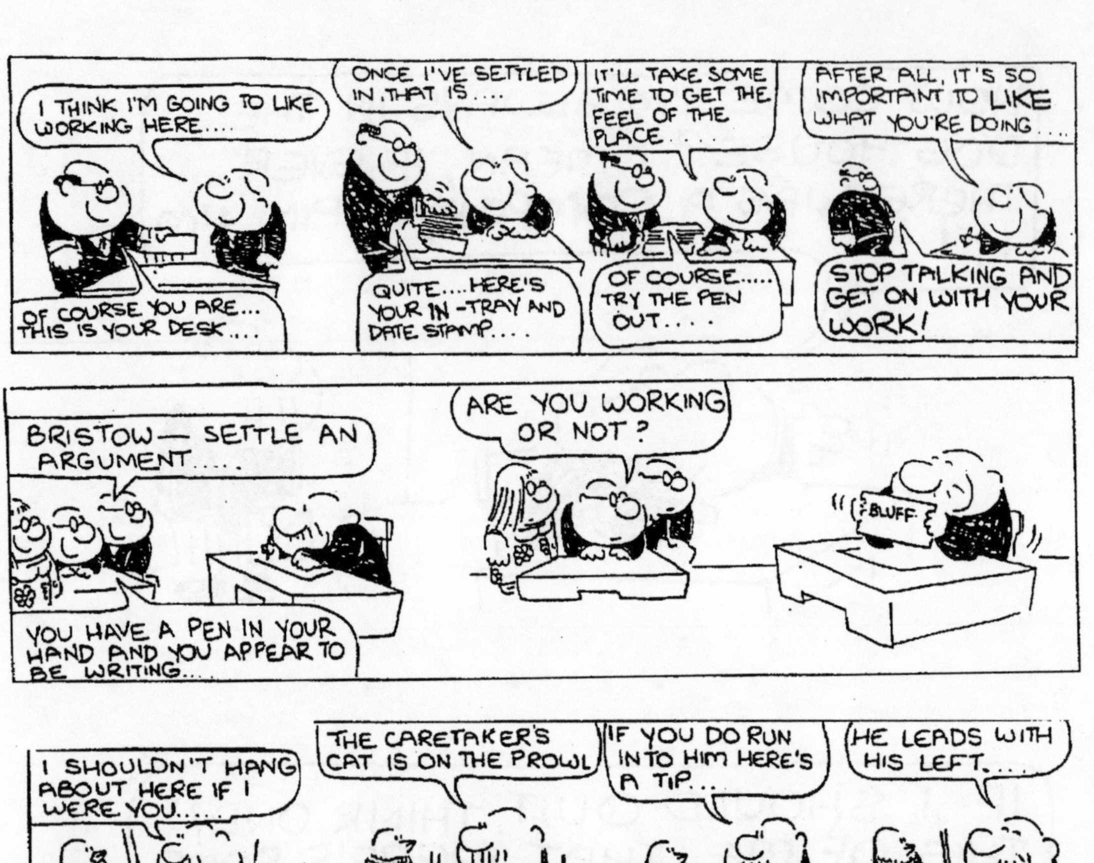

The above strip has remained in my mind, not because of the content, but the story behind it, for it was the first time I fell foul of the Unions.

In the 1960s the Unions (and there were a great number in the print trade) were all powerful. On the day in question I was showing a group of students how a comic strip eventually gets into the paper, and somehow or other found myself in the Compositor's room, where the strip was waiting to be dealt with. A trifle enthusiastically, I picked it up and brandished it, my triumph being suddenly dampened by one of the operators asking who I was and what was going on.

My explanation was cut short by a hastily convened meeting of officials and strip deemed 'blacked', the reason given that I was not a union member and therefore not allowed to pick up anything on that floor.

My protest that I was the creator and it was my property cut no ice.

'Blacked' it remained.

I put it in the following week.

YOU ARE LOOKING RATHER PLEASED WITH LIFE....
I AM.... I ACTUALLY LOOK FORWARD TO COMING TO WORK.....
IT'S THIS NEW COMPUTER... IT'S CHANGED NOT ONLY MY LIFE, BUT THAT OF THOSE AROUND ME... IT DOES **EVERYTHING**!
SOUNDS GREAT! HOW LONG HAVE YOU HAD THAT?
FIVE AND A HALF WEEKS...

SO IT'S A GOOD COMPUTER.. THE QUESTION IS — IS IT **USER FRIENDLY**?
THE FRIENDLIEST... BUT THEN IT SHOULD BE... A THING LIKE THIS DOESN'T COME CHEAP....
HOW MUCH MONEY ARE WE TALKING ABOUT?
£2000,000,000
BUT YOU GET ALL THE BITS AND PIECES.... THE CABLE... THE PLUG AND EVERYTHING..?
EVERYTHING. EXCEPT THE BATTERIES....
SO IT'S NOT ALL THAT EXPENSIVE REALLY....
NOT **REALLY**....

ARE YOU SERIOUSLY TELLING ME THAT TRAMP IN THE PARK INVENTED THE MODERN COMPUTER?
YES... HE WAS TELLING ME ABOUT IT....
HE GOT THE IDEA TWENTY YEARS AGO AND WORKED ON IT IN HIS SPARE TIME.... SPENT ALL HIS SAVINGS ON IT.... EVEN MORTGAGED HIS HOUSE TO PAY FOR THE COMPONENT PARTS....
SO WHY ISN'T HE RICH?
THE JAPANESE GOT HOLD OF IT....
USUAL STORY... BRITISH INVENTION...

STILL POURING THE STUFF DOWN, ARE WE, MR. BRISTOW?
POSTBOY — IN THIS LIFE OF OURS WE GET PRECIOUS LITTLE OF WHAT IS CALLED **QUALITY** TIME, AND WHAT LITTLE WE GET I LIKE TO SPEND DRINKING TEA....
PARDON ME FOR LIVING....!

I'D LIKE TO HAND IN THIS PAIR OF GLOVES...
LOST PROPERTY
THANK YOU SIR — NICE TO MEET AN HONEST MAN
LET'S SEE.... GENTS BROWN LEATHER, VERY DIRTY AND OILY... HOLES IN ALL FINGERS.
CAN I HAVE PARTICULARS OF HOW YOU FOUND THEM..?
SECOND CARRIAGE FROM THE FRONT... 5. 15 TO EAST WINCHLEY
THAT WOULD BE LAST NIGHT?
NO — ABOUT 2 WEEKS AGO....
I COULDN'T BRING THEM IN BEFORE — I WANTED TO FIT MY NEW GEAR BOX

Gentle reader,
After its winter sojourn in the sun this bird has lost its homing instinct and, confused and bewildered flies hither and thither.....
CRAAK! CRAAK!
If it could speak it would be crying "Where am I? Where am I?"
CRAAK! CRAAK!
Is there no salvation, or is he, like the Flying Dutchman, doomed to travel the world forever?
BRISTOW — GET ON WITH YOUR WORK!
CLICK!
CHIRRUP, CHIRRUP!

DON'T YOU EVER GET TIRED OF SITTING THERE DOING NOTHING...?
DON'T BE IMPERTINENT MY BOY....
WHEN YOU'RE OLDER YOU'LL REALISE ALL THE TIME I'M SITTING HERE APPARENTLY DOING NOTHING I'M CHIPPING AWAY AT THE ESTABLISHMENT.........

BRISTOW — HAVE YOU EVER THOUGHT THERE MUST BE MORE TO LIFE THAN THIS?
AND?
YES.... I'VE GIVEN THE MATTER A GREAT DEAL OF THOUGHT...
THE HONEST ANSWER IS THERE'S NOT THAT MUCH MORE....

LOOK AT IT OUT THERE...
LOVELY SUNSHINE.. AND I'M
STUCK IN A STUFFY OFFICE

WHAT WOULDN'T I GIVE TO
BE OUT THERE INSTEAD OF
ROTTING AWAY IN THIS DEAD
AND ALIVE HOLE ?

IT'S INHUMAN — THAT'S
WHAT IT IS — INHUMAN !

HELLO — THERE'S A SMALL
CROWD GATHERING IN THE
STREET... WONDER WHAT'S
GOING ON ?

CHAP IN AN OFFICE UP THERE GIVING A WONDERFUL IMPRESSION OF A CAGED LION....

SO MR. GORDON BLUE, OUR MASTER CHEF, HAS WRITTEN A COOKERY BOOK?
THAT'S RIGHT....
AND THE TITLE OF THIS TOME?
IT'S CALLED "GET THAT DOWN YOU!"
PROVISIONAL TITLE, ONE HOPES?
FOREWORD BY BILLY BUNTER...

THE GORGEOUS MISS PRETTY OF KLEENAPHONE IS IN THE OFFICE ACROSS THE ROAD AND GOOD HEAVENS! SHE'S WAVING AT ME!!
SHE'S NOT WAVING AT YOU — YOU FOOL.
SHE'S SHAKING HER DUSTER.......

MR. BRISTOW, CAN I ASK YOU A QUESTION?
FIRE AWAY, POSTBOY..
WHAT IS IT LIKE TO LIVE A MUNDANE EXISTENCE?
HOW SHOULD I KNOW? I'M STUCK IN THE OFFICE ALL DAY.....

PINCH ME, JONES.....
TELL ME THIS IS ALL A BAD DREAM.....

28. SPARE RIB.

NURSE — MR. BRISTOW IS SUFFERING FROM THE LOSS OF HIS **GIRLIE CALENDAR**...
TELL HIM TO TAKE A CHAIR...
REMOVE HIS JACKET AND ROLL UP HIS SLEEVE....

EXCUSE ME, MR. JONES — IT **IS** MR JONES I'M SPEAKING TO, ISN'T IT?
YOU KNOW MORE WAYS OF HURTING **ME**.......

JONES — MISS SUNMAN CLAIMS SHE LIVES FROM ONE **VALENTINE** DAY TO THE NEXT... EVERYTHING IN BETWEEN IS JUST A BLUR....
SO?
YOU DON'T FIND THAT SURPRISING?
NOT SPECIALLY....
SHE'S A **WOMAN**, ISN'T SHE?

MR. BRISTOW — IT MIGHT INTEREST YOU TO KNOW THAT YOUR NAME WAS MENTIONED IN THE TYPING POOL YESTERDAY....
IT WAS DECIDED THAT OF ALL THE MEN IN THE FIRM YOU ARE THE ONE WITH **CLERKABILITY**....
CLERKABILITY, EH? **CLERKABILITY**....
IS THAT GOOD OR BAD?

MR. BRISTOW — DO YOU KNOW MR. ARBUSSON OF ACCOUNTS?
ARBUSSON? YES, I KNOW HIM....
WE HAVE BEEN KNOWN TO LOCK HORNS ON THE ODD OCCASION.....

WHAT'S THE SUDDEN INTEREST IN MR. ARBUSSON?
HE MAKES ME NERVOUS... HE GIVES ME SMOULDERING GLANCES EVERY TIME I PASS HIS DESK....
SMOULDERING GLANCES, EH?
SOUNDS AS THOUGH HE'S LOSING HIS MARBLES.....

GOING TO THE ANNUAL CHRISTMAS DINNER AND DANCE NEXT WEEK?
I'LL SAY!
I WOULDN'T MISS IT.... IT'S MY ONE BIG NIGHT OF THE YEAR....
FUNNY THINGS WOMEN, AREN'T THEY?

WHAT IS HAPPENING, MR. BRISTOW?
ACCOUNTS HAVE STOLEN MY GIRLIE CALENDAR....
ALL THIS FUSS OVER A CALENDAR THAT DEMEANS THE ROLE OF —
STOP RIGHT THERE!
A GIRLIE CALENDAR HAS NOTHING TO DO WITH SEX....

29. SOMETHING SEASONAL...

I'VE BUTTERFLIES IN MY STOMACH
ME, TOO
I CAN'T WAIT
WHAT'S GOING ON?
OF COURSE THEY SHOULD
I STILL SAY THEY SHOULD HAVE DONE IT EARLIER....
BIG DAY, TODAY
THIS EVENING THEY ARE SWITCHING THE LIGHTS ON IN THE CORRIDORS......

...THE LAST ITEM ON THE AGENDA IS THE FIRM'S CHRISTMAS DINNER AND DANCE.....
HOW MANY TICKETS HAVE BEEN SOLD SO FAR?
764
DAMN AND BLAST! THAT MEANS WE'LL HAVE TO GO THROUGH WITH IT....

I'M FED UP TO THE BACK TEETH WITH THESE LAST MINUTE SHOPPERS.....
AFTER A HARD DAY AT THE OFFICE I HAD TO STAND ALL THE WAY HOME....
MY USUAL CORNER SEAT WAS OCCUPIED BY AN 18 LB TURKEY...

IT'S JUST A REMINDER ABOUT THE FIRM'S CHRISTMAS DINNER AND DANCE.....
SEEMS THEY ARE TRYING TO CUT DOWN THE NUMBERS
NO HARD HATS, OVERALLS OR WORKING BOOTS....

MY WORD, JONES— YOU'VE DONE WELL FOR CHRISTMAS CARDS THIS YEAR...
NOT BAD... NOT BAD...
YOU'VE DONE EVEN BETTER THAN I HAVE..
REALLY? WELL YES, I SUPPOSE I HAVE..

I'D SAY THAT'S AN OFFICE RECORD.... YOU'RE MORE POPULAR THAN I THOUGHT...
PLEASE, BRISTOW— YOU EMBARRASS ME....

I'LL EMBARRASS YOU STILL FURTHER.. THIS TOP ROW OF CARDS READS, FROM LEFT TO RIGHT, HAPPY CHRISTMAS '64 – EASTER GREETINGS GET WELL SOON... HAPPY BIRTHDAY...

R.L. DIESTER-PERRY CO. LTD

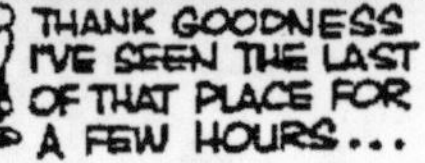
THANK GOODNESS I'VE SEEN THE LAST OF THAT PLACE FOR A FEW HOURS...

HOLY MACKEREL!

PUT THOSE COINS AWAY AND DON'T EVER LET ME CATCH YOU PLAYING DESK TOP FOOTBALL AGAIN!!!!
YES, MR FUDGE!
CERTAINLY MR. FUDGE..
RIGHTAWAY MR. FUDGE..
SLAM!
WE'LL CALL IT A DRAW.....
RUBBISH — I WAS A GOAL UP!
YES, BUT THERE WAS STILL FIVE MINUTES TO GO.....
WHAT DO WE DO? THERE IS NOTHING IN THE RULEBOOK ABOUT THE BOSS COMING IN SUDDENLY AND CUTTING SHORT THE GAME.....
OF COURSE THERE IS — IT'S THE CLERICAL EQUIVALENT OF THE CROWD INVADING THE PITCH.....

IT'S A SHAME OLD FUDGE INTERRUPTED OUR DESK TOP FOOTBALL MATCH....
PITY HE DIDN'T GIVE US TIME TO FINISH...
ON THE CONTRARY...... LET'S THANK OUR LUCKY STARS HE CAME IN WHEN HE DID....
WHAT DO YOU MEAN?
IF HE'D COME IN A MINUTE LATER HE'D HAVE CAUGHT US EXCHANGING SHIRTS....

OLD FUDGE DOESN'T MISS A TRICK..... YOU'RE NEVER ALONE...
CROSS TO THE FAR SIDE OF THE ROOM AND YOU CAN FEEL HIM KEEPING TABS ON YOU...
CROUCH BEHIND YOUR DESK YOU'RE STILL UNDER SURVEILLANCE...
HIDE BEHIND THE FILING CABINET AND YOU CAN FEEL HIM WATCHING YOU.....
PEER THROUGH HIS KEYHOLE AND YOU'RE EYEBALL TO EYEBALL.......

BRIGHTLY SHONE THE MOON AT NIGHT
THO' THE FROST WAS CRUEL
WHEN A POOR MAN CAME IN SIGHT.....

RAFFLE TICKET MR. BRISTOW?
CERTAINLY, MISS SUNMAN... WHAT ARE THE PRIZES...?
THERE ARE FIFTY PRIZES.... THE FIRST IS A CIGARETTE LIGHTER....
FIFTY PRIZES?-WHAT'S THE LAST?
YOU GET TO BE A CLERK IN THE BUYING DEPARTMENT......
DINNER & DANCE

POSTBOY — TAKE MY ADVICE AND COME TO THE DINNER AND DANCE......
NO WAY! — WHO WANTS TO GO PARTY FULL OF GERIATRIC WHITE COLLAR WORKERS...?
SUIT YOURSELF... BUT I'M ONLY TELLING YOU FOR YOUR OWN GOOD...
ANYONE THAT DOESN'T ATTEND THE DINNER AND DANCE IS AUTOMATICALLY PASSED OVER WHEN IT COMES TO PROMOTION....

NURSE — COME QUICKLY — AND BRING A STRAIT JACKET!
WE FOUND A CRAZY MAN IN THE BROOM CUPBOARD THIS MORNING AND WE ARE STRUGGLING TO APPREHEND HIM.... OF COURSE HE'S CRAZY!
HE'S TURNING OUT COUNTERFEIT TICKETS FOR THE FIRM'S DINNER AND DANCE....

WHAT ARE YOU GOING TO WEAR TO THE CHRISTMAS DINNER AND —
DO YOU MIND? I WAS JUST ASKING MR. BRISTOW FOR THE LAST DANCE...
SORRY — I'LL COME BACK LATER....
JONES — BODY ARMOUR!

FIRM'S DINNER AND DANCE — HERE WE COME...
GASP!
JONES!!!!
WHAT'S WRONG?
WHEW! YOU FRIGHTENED THE LIFE OUT OF ME WITH THAT PINK SHIRT AND PINK TIE.....
FOR A SECOND I THOUGHT IT WAS A PLUNGING NECKLINE!!

COME ON, BRISTOW —
NO WAY!
JOHNSON ON THE NEXT TABLE PULLED ONE AND GOT A PAPER HAT, A MOTTO AND HIS P.45.....

THERE'S ALWAYS ONE! AT EVERY PARTY THERE'S ALWAYS SOMEONE WHO HAS TO SPOIL THINGS!
WHO IS IT THIS TIME?
BRISTOW OF BUYING
HE WON'T EAT HIS GREENS.....

OOH, LOOK — I'VE GOT THE WISHBONE.....
YAWN!
LUCKY OLD YOU...
COME ALONG NOW, MR. BRISTOW... PULL IT WITH ME .... THE ONE THAT GETS THE BIGGEST END GETS THE WISH...
YAWN!
VERY WELL — IF YOU INSIST...
READY STEADY — NOW!
LUCKY OLD YOU....
MAKE A WISH...
I WISH THAT ON THE STROKE OF MIDNIGHT YOU'D TURN INTO A BEAUTIFUL PRINCESS.....

STAND ASIDE, LADIES... LET ME SEE HOW THE STAFF ARE ENJOYING THEIR MAGNIFICENT CHRISTMAS DINNER...
SUCCULENT SLICES OF TURKEY, STUFFING, CRISP GOLDEN ROAST POTATOES, TENDER GARDEN PEAS, FRESH BRUSSEL SPROUTS AND CRANBERRY SAUCE...
LEAVE IT — WE CAN ALWAYS EAT ON THE WAY HOME
THERE'S AN ALL NIGHT CAFE ROUND THE CORNER
WHAT TIME DOES THE CHINESE TAKEAWAY CLOSE?
THE STATION BUFFET WILL STILL BE OPEN......

THIS BUTCH AFTER-SHAVE IS THE BEST CHRISTMAS PRESENT I'VE EVER HAD...
SNIFF! SNIFF!
IT'S ABOUT TIME YOU GOT BACK.....
I'VE BEEN HERE ALL MORNING..
DON'T GIVE ME THAT...
I KNOW FOR A FACT THAT YOU'VE BEEN THROUGH THE TYPING POOL... DOWN TO THE STORES... ACCOUNTS... INVOICING...
SNIFF! SNIFF!

30. LISTEN TO THIS....

I always thought that Bristow would be good on radio. Or TV. Or film. Or theatre. Or anywhere except a newspaper, where lack of space did not allow the character to develop in the way I had imagined. I am, I suppose, the only living person that knows that Bristow is a TALKER, but when the strip began, because of the restrictions imposed by the space provided, I had a choice. This was to either cut down on his office space or the verbiage, and because the reader needed to know what the central character looked like, I was forced to go for the latter.

When I say he is a TALKER, I am understating it. He has the gift of the gab in spades. Dominate a London dinner table? No problem. Arouse a rabble? Kidstuff. He is a wonderful, hypnotic, spell binding, eat-your-heart-out Hitler, crowd pleaser. His speech is as flowery as Cyrano, his sentences poetic as Quixote, and even in the confines of the strip cartoon he uses words and phrases coined from some of the great names of this or any other century. Shakespeare, Johnson, Tolstoy, Hugo, Balzac, Wilde, Boswell, Zola, you name 'em, he quotes them. Imagine a man who has a command of the English language and who peppers his conversation with ideas and theories lifted from the minds of such luminaries as Einstein, Plato, Socrates, Freud, you name 'em, in comes the pepper. Upmarket? Possibly. You don't understand it? Probably. BUT, and here is the point I am trying to make, imagine a man with such a mind forced to live out his life within the confines of that rectangle in which he is forced to act out his daily office routine. Imagine his pent up frustration at not being allowed to let it all out because of sheer lack of space. Imagine this man given full rein! He could rule the world.

That's why I thought radio was a good idea. Expand the frontiers, as it were. Wow the listeners, so to speak. Pound the lobes.

Alas, it was not to be.

When I mentioned the idea of a daily 'strip cartoon for radio' to Jonathan James Moore, the then head of BBC comedy, I think the idea appealed to him. But, as always in the transition to the spoken word and the BBC way of thinking, it was decided to make it into a half-hour comedy series.

This requires something in the nature of a plot, and here a clash of interest asserted itself.

I am good on plots. Strong, even. I am so good that due to the intricacies of those I set down for the radio series there was no room for Bristow to get a word in edgeways . . .

THAT DICKY DABBS CAN'T PULL THE WOOL OVER MY EYES....

THOSE SPARKLING EYES AND THAT AMUSING AND WHOLLY IRREVERENT ATTITUDE TO EVERYTHING AND EVERYONE DOESN'T FOOL ME....

I LOOK UPON HIS OBVIOUS ENJOYMENT OF LIFE AS A CRY FOR HELP.......

JONES — I'M NOT FEELING TOO GOOD.....GET ME TO **SICK BAY**....

THE SUN WAS BEATING DOWN ON MY DESK TOP....MY **IN-TRAY** WAS SHIMMERING IN THE HEAT — AND THEN ALL AT ONCE IT LOOKED **EMPTY**! I HAD FINISHED ALL MY WORK!!! I BLINKED — AND THE **IN-TRAY** WAS SUDDENLY FULL OF WORK AGAIN!!!!

IT'S CALLED A MIRAGE....

I ALWAYS ENJOY TAKING A STROLL THROUGH THE MACHINE SHOP...

WHUMP! WHIRR! WHUMP!
CRASH! CRASH!
WHIRR! WHUMP!

IT'S THE ONLY PLACE I GET ANY RESPECT....

WHIRR! CRASH!
CRASH! WHIRR!
WHUMP! WH WHUMP!

TO THEM I'M THE BIG NOISE FROM UPSTAIRS!

WHUMP! WHIRR! WHUMP! CRASH!
WHUMP! CRASH! CRASH
CRASH!
WHIRR! WHUMP!
WHUMP! CRASH!

I THINK YOU WASTE TOO MUCH TIME ON THAT BIRD, BRISTOW...
WHAT IS A BIRD, AFTER ALL? A BIRD IS JUST AN EGGS WAY OF MAKING OTHER EGGS....
DON'T LISTEN TO THE NASTY MAN....

GOOD MORNING, MISS.... CAN I HELP YOU?
YOU CAN HELP BY BEING QUIET....
I ONLY TOOK A JOB HERE TO KEEP AN EYE ON MY BOY FRIEND, WHO WORKS IN THE OFFICE ACROSS THE STREET.... DOES THAT SURPRISE YOU?
NOT AT ALL...
BEST REASON I EVER HEARD FOR ANYONE TAKING A JOB IN THIS DUMP.....

WHO WAS THAT GIRL YOU WERE TALKING TO?
MISS PRINTEMPS....
SHE TELLS ME SHE ONLY GOT A JOB HERE TO KEEP AN EYE ON HER BOYFRIEND WHO WORKS IN THE OFFICE ACROSS THE STREET....
WHICH ONE IS THE BOYFRIEND?
THE ONE GIVING US THE FINGER....

THAT'S YOUR BOYFRIEND IN THE OFFICE ACROSS THE STREET, IS IT?
YUP!
NICE LOOKING CHAP— IF YOU LIKE THAT KIND OF FACE....
SOMETHING FUNNY ABOUT THE WAY HE WALKS, TOO...
HE STAGGERS AROUND THE ROOM LIKE A CHICKEN STUNNED BY A MALLET......

31. BRISTOW AND SHOWBIZ.

In spite of what I have written before, the radio series was a success and ran to a fourth series. We were fortunate enough to secure a strong cast, with Michael Williams playing Bristow. Interestingly enough, he had no idea he was playing a strip cartoon character until after the second series. When I mentioned this he was genuinely surprised. 'I had no idea,' he said. (Could he have been acting? I don't think so.) But he played it until his death earlier this year, with excellent reviews.

It was not the first time Bristow had flirted with showbiz. After the strip had been running a few years I was approached by David Susskind, an American entrepreneur, who asked whether he could set up a Bristow film. A film called **The Apartment** *had just been released, its theme being a clerk who lent his apartment to senior executives of the firm that employed him. Another 'office' film was planned with Jack Lemmon repeating his role of a clerk. They wanted Jack Lemmon to play Bristow. I turned down the idea, saying he was not right. The only man who could play Bristow was Richard Attenborough. I had seen* **The Dock Brief** *starring Attenborough and Peter Sellers and thought he was perfect for the part. (He was not interested, I gather, being preoccupied with getting his 'Ghandi' project off the ground.)*

It was not the first time a suggestion that Bristow might transfer to a medium other than newspapers had been made. A short stage version starring Freddie Jones and Anna Quayle had been tried out at the ICA in the Mall and although receiving good notices, did not have producers hammering on my door waving cheque books.

Some years later a second effort to make a film was attempted, and this time showed promise. A noted screenwriter was brought in. Alan Hackney had just written **I'm All Right, Jack** *and was a hot property. Arthur Lowe was mentioned and we met on a number of occasions. I approved. Things were looking good. But the timing was not right. Arthur was beginning to get involved with something that was going to be called* **Dad's Army**. *That's showbiz . . .*

EVENING STANDARD, THURSDAY, JANUARY 14, 1971—17

MILTON SHULMAN
at the theatre

Bristow—to the life!

IN THE conglomerate world of the Chester-Perry empire, the ingenuity and energy of the staff is chiefly devoted to discovering ways and means of avoiding work.

Most adept at earning a living by not really trying is Bristow, the cunning loafer of the buying department, whose machinations against the sales staff, adventures with the typing pool and intrigues with the tea lady, have for years delighted readers of Frank Dickens's strip cartoon in this paper.

Together with Michael Bakewell, Frank Dickens has now transferred Bristow and his striped - trousered colleagues to the stage at the Institute of Contemporary Arts. The move is an undiluted success.

Although Freddie Jones is twice as tall as the original, everything else about him from his toothbrush moustache, the predatory eyes, the humped posture of resignation as he surveys the debris of the tea-trolley, conveys the seedy spirit of Bristow.

This hour-long play begins with Bristow waking to the rapture of it being Sunday morning and a day off work, only shortly to realise—"Holy Mackerel!"—that it's Monday.

In the office he sadly contemplates the prospect of eight hours of Chester-Perrydom ahead of him, converts this to 28,800 seconds and proceeds to count the seconds away for the rest of the play.

The entire day is spent over rumours and counter-rumours that Chester-Perry is to take over Myles and Rudge Ltd. who in turn are to be taken over by Bloggs Bros.

Like bowler-hatted rats deserting a sinking skyscraper, everyone is on the phone trying to get himself a job somewhere else. Most of the news is conveyed through the tea-girl who quotes Omar Khayyam when the strain of dispensing rock-hard fairy cakes becomes too much.

"Will you get me my opposite number at Bloggs?" says Bristow to the telephone girl. "You'll be wanting the tea-boy then," comes the irreverent reply.

As a secretary anguished over the prospect of having to makes six carbon copies, as a saucy telephone operator, as a traffic warden whose views on every subject coincide precisely with those of the Minister of Transport, Anna Quayle oozes a hilarious variety of mannerisms.

At the moment the cast seems a little hesitant about their lines, but when they get their timing perfected Bristow will undoubtedly be an endearing and funny dramatized memo of this successful comic strip.

ICA

Naseem Khan

Bristow

"BRISTOW," the lunchtime show at the ICA, is visually—except for Anna Quayle's flaming red hair—a black and white play. It's the pinstripes, bowler, umbrella, and briefcase world of Frank Dickens which he explores in his daily strip-cartoon in the "Evening Standard." The trip from newsprint to theatre boards is not without its risks, but Bristow comes through with aplomb. It's a delightful, deft, wicked 50 minutes, for which much of the credit must go to Michael Bakewell's direction.

He has resisted any temptation to naturalise the well-known characters, but built upon the pithy throwaway elliptical quality of the cartoon. The strip's shorthand becomes the style of the play. Each punchline (coming regularly, like the cartoon, on, as it were, every fourth box) almost carries with it a stylised wink to the audience, like an old-fashioned clown. The cast plays it with panache, while Freddie Jones as Bristow uncannily achieves he beady-eyed gleam of his cartoon ounterpart.

Frank Dickens and Michael Bakewell ve devised a drama-filled situation for m. Doom hangs over the Chester ry building where Bristow has his e. A takeover bid has been made Myles and Rudge across the way. ternation spreads: Myles and e employees are rumoured to be ustard," and so obviously some of the stodge of Chester Perry will have to go.

Bristow, the stodge of the stodge, sets a devious plan afoot to prove his mustard potential, which is constantly foiled by incursions of Miss Sunman of the typing pool (Anna Quayle), the tea lady (Anna Quayle), the telephonist (Anna Quayle), his colleague Jones (Graham Roberts) or the trendy office boy (Matthew Corbett). How this battle of big business and high finance is resolved—and why indeed the meter lady (Anna Quayle) has played such a vital part in its inception—cannot be revealed. But it's mustard.

Guardian 14 January

NO POINT IN TRYING TO TALK TO BRISTOW TODAY...
THE LIGHTS ARE ON BUT THERE'S NO ONE IN....

CHEEK UP, LAD... A BOY OF YOUR AGE SHOULDN'T BE DOWN IN THE MOUTH....
MR. BRISTOW — JUDGING BY WHAT THE LADS IN THE POSTROOM SAY, THERE'S NOT MUCH FUTURE IN THIS JOB.....
YOU DON'T WANT TO LISTEN TO THAT BUNCH OF NE'ER-DO-WELLS IN THE POSTROOM WHAT DO THEY KNOW?
OF COURSE THERE'S A FUTURE, AND IT'S A BRIGHT AND SHINY FUTURE — LOOK AT ME!!!

JONES — WHAT DO YOU THINK OF THIS IDEA?
WHILST NOT SUFFERING AN ACCIDENT ON COMPANY PREMISES AND IN COMPANY TIME, MY STANDARD OF FITNESS HAS DETERIATED AND I WOULD LIKE TO PUT IN A CLAIM FOR SAME.....
TRY IT....

BRISTOW — THIS PLACE IS THE BEE'S KNEES.....
I'VE BEEN AROUND, BRISTOW, AND TAKE IT FROM ME, THERE AREN'T MANY MUNICIPAL PARKS LIKE THIS ONE...
YOU CAN SAY THAT AGAIN, JONES... FLOWERS... TREES... BUSHES... HEDGES... COWS... GOATS... TRACTORS....

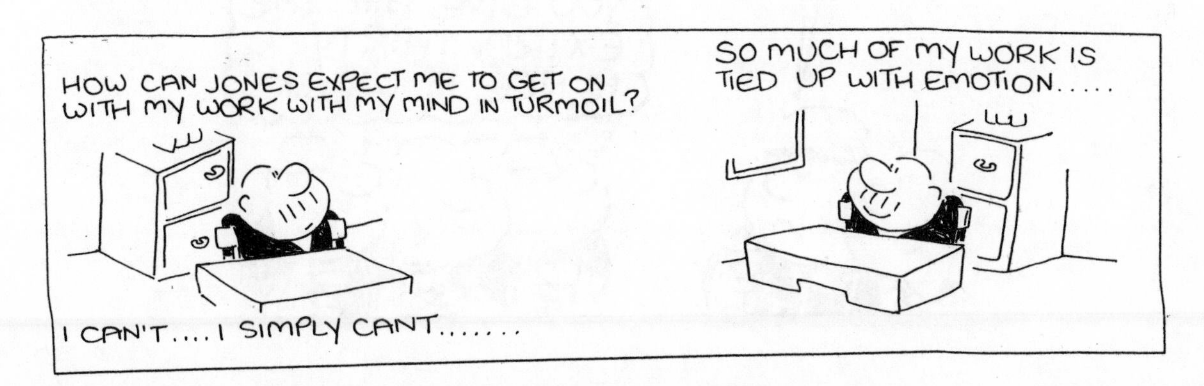
HOW CAN JONES EXPECT ME TO GET ON WITH MY WORK WITH MY MIND IN TURMOIL?
I CAN'T.... I SIMPLY CANT.......
SO MUCH OF MY WORK IS TIED UP WITH EMOTION.....

IT IS ALWAYS A SAD OCCASION WHEN SOMEONE LEAVES A FIRM, PARTICULARLY ONE WHO IS AS WELL THOUGHT OF AS MR. DAVIS. AS HEAD OF HIS DEPARTMENT I CAN SAY FROM THE BOTTOM OF MY HEART THAT MR. DAVIS WILL BE SORELY MISSED. HE WAS LOYAL, COURTEOUS, PUNCTUAL, EFFICIENT AND HARDWORKING. ONE OF THOSE RARE BEINGS OF WHOM IT CAN BE SAID 'HE IS TRULY INDISPENSABLE'

SO WHY DIDN'T YOU GIVE HIM THE EXTRA THIRTY PENCE A WEEK?

HASN'T THE DAY GONE QUICKLY?

ONLY ANOTHER FIVE MINUTES AND IT'LL BE '**FED UP TO THE BACK TEETH**' TIME...

32. BACK TO THE COALFACE...

THIS IS A GREAT FIRM TO WORK FOR, SIR . . I LOVE IT HERE . . .
I TAKE IT YOU HAD LUNCH IN THE FIRM'S CANTEEN . . . .
HOW DID YOU KNOW ?
STANDARD PRACTICE...
THEY SLIP SOMETHING INTO THE CRÉME BRULEE . . . .

YOUNG MAN — WE MUST CONGRATULATE YOU ON THE HIGH STANDARD OF WORK WHICH YOU HAVE SET ON YOUR FIRST DAY WITH THE COMPANY... WELL DONE!
THIS IS THE CHESTER-PERRY JOKE LINE.....

MR. BRISTOW -- I'LL MAKE A VERY GOOD POSTBOY WHEN I'VE FOUND MY FEET...
LISTEN TO ME, KID...
A RELATIVE OF THE FIRM'S FOUNDER DOESN'T HAVE TO FIND HIS FEET.....

ISN'T IT GREAT ? THE OTHER KIDS IN THE POSTROOM DON'T MIND ME BEING RELATED TO THE FIRM'S FOUNDER....
WHY SHOULD THEY ?
NEPOTISM IS LOOKED ON FAVOURABLY IN THIS FIRM . .

IT'S INCREDIBLE...

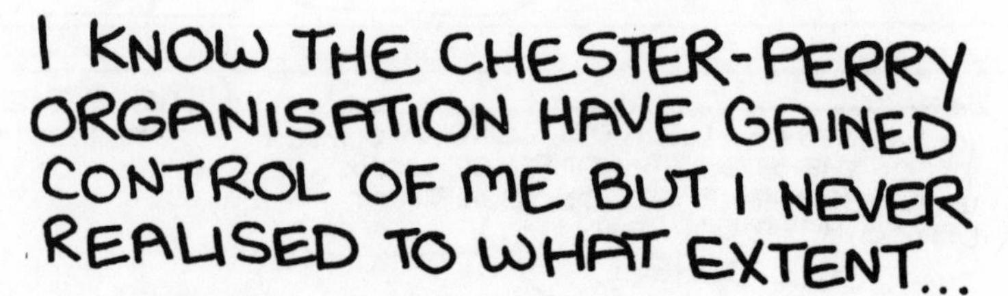

I KNOW THE CHESTER-PERRY ORGANISATION HAVE GAINED CONTROL OF ME BUT I NEVER REALISED TO WHAT EXTENT...
THIS TEA IS DELICIOUS!

GULP!

EVEN MY TASTE BUDS HAVE BEEN BRAINWASHED....

MR. BRISTOW WON'T MIND —JUST ASK HIM...
YOU SURE HE WON'T MIND?
NO—JUST ASK.... HE MIGHT SURPRISE YOU....
EVERYTHING MIXES TOGETHER IN HIS HEAD: WORK, WOMEN, MEDALS, ART.....

I CAN'T BELIEVE ANYONE COULD BE SO NOSEY...
I WAS HOLDING JONES'S BLOTTER UP TO THE MIRROR TO SEE WHAT HE'S BEEN WORKING ON THIS MORNING AND WOULD YOU BELIEVE IT — I TURN ROUND AND CATCH HEWITT ACTUALLY LOOKING OVER MY SHOULDER..........

HELLO — A NEW SHOP...
EVERYTHING FOR THE OFFICE WORKER, EH? WELL, LET'S SEE....
SO FAR SO GOOD..
LEAD SOLED BOOTS EXERCISE ON YOUR WAY TO WORK.
LIKE IT! LIKE IT!!
LIGHTWEIGHT RUNNING SHOES GET HOME EARLY!

WELL, WELL, LOOK WHO'S HERE...
IT'S THE BIRD THAT SITS ON MY WINDOW SILL FROM DAWN TILL DUSK...
SHOO! CATS!! MIAW! SHOO!!
I DON'T WANT TO ENCOURAGE THESE SOCIAL VISITS...
WE SEE ENOUGH OF EACH OTHER ALL DAY AT THE OFFICE!

YOU'RE A PAIN IN THE NECK, BRISTOW. EVER SINCE YOU HAD A WORD OF PRAISE FROM FUDGE YOU'VE BEEN UNBEARABLE....
FROM BEING A DYED-IN-THE-WOOL REBEL YOU'VE BECOME A FAWNING SYCOPHANT...
WATCH YOUR WORDS, JONES, OR YOU MAY BE SORRY ONE DAY..... YOU KNOW THE OLD SAYING....
A SYCOPHANT NEVER FORGETS...

WHY SHOULD ACCOUNTS PEOPLE BE THE WAY THEY ARE..?
BECAUSE THEY WORK WITH MONEY, THAT'S WHY.....
THEY ARE VICTIMS OF THE SYSTEM... TERRIFIED OF MAKING A MISTAKE...
SLIP OF THE PEN OR A LAPSE IN CONCENTRATION AND THEY COULD BE BANGED UP FOR LIFE....

HELLO — WHAT HAVE WE HERE?
NEW CROCKERY... THINGS ARE LOOKING UP...
LIKE THE NEW PLATES? CHESTER-PERRY WILLOW PATTERN
CHESTER-PERRY WILLOW PATTERN?
THERE — THERE — THERE... TELLS A STORY...
TWO EMPLOYEES SNEAKING OUT EARLY OVER A HUMP BACK BRIDGE WITH SIR REGINALD IN HOT PURSUIT........

THIS PLACE IS LIKE AN OVEN....I'M BEGINNING TO FEEL QUITE DROUSY.....
I THINK I'LL OPEN A WINDOW BEFORE I DOZE OFF..........
Z

COUGH! SPLUTTER! COUGH, COUGH! COUGH! COUGH! COUGH! COUGH!
TOO MANY CIGARETTES NORAH?
I'M A NON SMOKER
I'VE BEEN DUSTING MR. BRISTOW'S OUT TRAY......

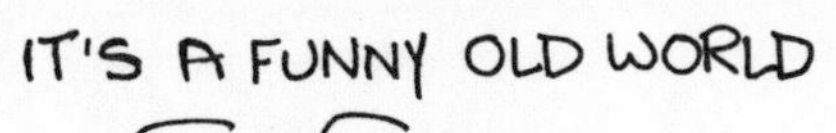
IT'S A FUNNY OLD WORLD

ALTHOUGH I'M IN A DESPERATE HURRY I STILL CANNOT RUSH MY BREAKFAST....

I HAVE TO SAVOUR AND DWELL ON EVERY MORSEL THAT PASSES MY LIPS...

WORKING FOR THE CHESTER-PERRY ORGANISATION I EAT EVERY BREAKFAST AS THO' IT WERE MY LAST...

LOOKING AT YOU I SEE A HIGHLY INSECURE MAN WHO IS FIGHTING TO HOLD DOWN HIS JOB....
ARE YOU A PSYCHIATRIST?
NO — A PASSENGER LIKE YOURSELF...
BUT EVERY MORNING AS THE TRAIN PULLS IN YOU START TO SHAKE....

JONES — BE SERIOUS... DO I LOOK LIKE A HIGHLY INSECURE MAN FIGHTING TO HOLD HIS JOB DOWN?
WEEEEEEEL...

MISS SUNMAN — I MET A MAN ON THE TRAIN TODAY WHO SAID I LOOKED LIKE A MAN FIGHTING TO HOLD HIS JOB DOWN...
I KNOW HIM.!! I KNOW THE MAN.!! DUGGIE BROWN...
UNCANNY, THE WAY HE GETS IT RIGHT EVERY TIME.....

I HATE THE WINTER... IT'S DARK WHEN WE ARRIVE AND DARK WHEN WE LEAVE....

MIND YOU — IT DOES HAVE ITS COMPENSATIONS.... BEFORE I START WORK I CAN SIT BACK, GAZE OUT OF THE WINDOW AND WATCH THE DAWN BREAKING!

A COLD, PALE MOON RIDES HIGH IN THE SKY....
BARE TREES BOW BEFORE THE ICY EAST WIND...

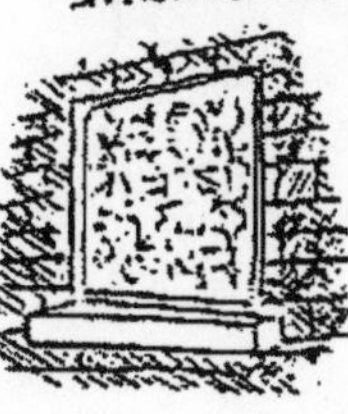
JACK FROST DANCES ON ROOF AND PAVEMENT, SPANGLING THE WINDOWS..

AND WELL-WRAPPED CITIZENS SCURRY HOME TO THE WARMTH OF THE HEARTH....

MEANWHILE, IN THE CHESTER-PERRY BUILDING A LAMP BURNS FAR INTO THE NIGHT...
TWO HOURS OVERTIME AT TIME AND A HALF...

YOU CARRY ON ENJOYING YOURSELVES OUT THERE - EATING, DRINKING AND WATCHING TV...
I'D RATHER BE ON OVERTIME AND LINE MY POCKETS....

I'M COINING IT AT TIME AND A HALF... ABSOLUTELY COINING IT..

YOU CAN SMILE NOW, BUT IF I CARRY ON AT THIS RATE, SOME DAY ALL THIS COULD BE MINE..

IN FORTY THREE MILLION SIX HUNDRED AND TWENTY SEVEN YEARS THIS COULD ALL BE MINE, I TELL YOU....

AH, WELL - NOT LONG TO GO NOW.... IT'S BEEN A LONG DAY. BUT IT WAS WORTH IT...

I SHAN'T BE SORRY TO GO HOME AND GET SOME SLEEP...
YAWN

TO SLEEP...
Z

PERCHANCE TO DREAM...
TWO AND A HALF HOURS AT TIME AND A HALF...

YOU'VE PICKED A GOOD TIME OF THE YEAR TO START...
BUYING DEPT

IT'S THE OVERTIME SEASON... IT MEANS WE FINISH EARLIER...
Z

LESS TO DUST....
Z

LET'S GET BACK TO ORDER NUMBER D.B. 355
YOU SEEM TO TAKE YOUR JOB VERY SERIOUSLY....

BELIEVE ME — I DON'T.... SPEAKING PERSONALLY, I DON'T CARE IF WE NEVER SEND YOU THE STUFF...
FROM MY POINT OF VIEW I DON'T CARE IF WE NEVER RECEIVE IT....

IT'S A KIND OF STALEMATE, ISN'T IT?
GUESS SO...

WILL YOU KINDLY LEAVE MY WINDOW ALONE? I DON'T WANT IT OPEN UNTIL SPRING...
DAMN FRESH AIR FIENDS! THE PLACE IS FREEZING...
STORES?— SEND UP A DOZEN BRICKS.... SOME SAND, SOME CEMENT AND A JUG OF WATER....

BRISTOW — ARE YOU SERIOUSLY TELLING ME THAT YOU ARE HAVING A DIAMOND IN YOUR NOSE AND INTEND TO WEAR AN EARRING?
I AM...
ONLY FOR THE ONE NIGHT...
IT'S THE FIRM'S CHRISTMAS DINNER AND DANCE IN THREE WEEK'S TIME.....

I DON'T KNOW HOW YOU'VE GOT THE NERVE TO ACCEPT WAGES—
I'LL HAVE YOU KNOW I WORK HARD FOR—
COME OFF IT! YOU DON'T DO A STROKE AND YOU KNOW IT!
HARDLY A DAY PASSES THAT I DON'T WONDER WHAT YOU'LL SAY TO SAINT PETER WHEN YOU ARRIVE AT THE PEARLY GATES.....

MR. BRISTOW — ABOUT THIS LETTER....
YOU'LL HAVE TO SPEAK UP— HE'S DEEP IN THOUGHT.....
I'LL LEAVE IT TILL LATER... I WOULDN'T WANT TO DISTURB ANYONE WHO IS DEEP IN THOUGHT...
YOU WON'T DISTURB HIM....
EVEN WHEN HE'S DEEP IN THOUGHT HIS MIND IS A BLANK....

I'VE BEEN THINKING... THERE'S ABSOLUTELY NOTHING TO STOP ME WALKING OUT THROUGH THAT DOOR AND JUST NEVER COMING BACK...

SO WHY DON'T I DO IT? I'VE NO COMMITMENTS...NO **TIES**...ALL I'VE GOT TO DO IS TO SUMMON UP THE COURAGE TO MAKE THE FINAL BREAK.... BY GEORGE I'LL DO IT! I'LL DAMN WELL DO IT!

SPLAT!
SPLAT!
FOILED AGAIN....

THE STUPID THING IS TRYING TO RACE US....
DIDDLEY DEE!
DIDDLEY DAH!
DIDDLEY DEE!
DIDDLEY DAH!
DIDDLEY DEE!
DAH!
DIDDLEY DEE!
HE DOESN'T REALISE WE TRAVEL AS THE CROW FLIES..

17
DAH!
DIDDLEY DEE!
DDLEY DAH!

P.S. ALL SINGING, ALL DANCING.

I have always loved musicals, and have always seen Bristow up there on the podium, alongside **Guys and Dolls** *and* **My Fair Lady**. *The forthcoming production will undoubtedly bear me out, but there is one slight qualm, and I can do nothing about this.*

The fact that the Bristow, when selected, may be no great shakes as a singer, is of no importance whatsoever. Whoever plays the part can talk his way through the numbers, with the lyrics I have penned for him and will have no problems from that angle. The only problem is the music, and I am not referring to the quality, which is of the highest order, as is everything written by Clement Ishmail, who conducts the orchestra for the smash hit **The Lion King**.

Clement appreciates the effect that a large orchestra can bring to a production and likes his music to be heard from the back row of the stalls. My real qualm is that if they play anything loud, the words will be drowned out . . .

Let us therefore set down in words Bristow's opening number, in the event that should anything untoward happen, something will remain to prove that, like the closing lines of Lerner and Loewe's **Camelot**, *we did exist . . .*

BRISTOW:
(SINGS)

I have to put on a weskit
'N be at my desk it
Nine on the dot.
I don't come alive
Till quarter to five
'N then not a lot!
Someone points to pen and ink
I can't speak
I'm tickled pink.

Where's that memo?
Need you ask it?
Pass me my wastepaper basket
Nose to grindstone
All that stuff?
Leave it out
I've had enough
Where's that (SEARCHES FOR WORD) *thingy?*
Oh, let's face it
We can easily replace it.

SOUNDS OF TEA TROLLEY OUTSIDE.

Mrs Purdy, what a treasure!
Trundles round dispensing pleasure.
On her trolley, next the spoons,
Stand in heaps, her macaroons,
Doughnuts, eclairs, whey hey hey!
Can't wait to put those things away.

I like coffee
I like tea
More, more, more, more!
It suits me.
With or without
Keep pouring it out
Impetuously.

I don't aspire
To be Chief Buyer
Or impress the powers that be –
There's a man here started yesterday
And he's in charge of me!

Tea and biscuits?
Yes sirree
Yum, yum, yum, yum!
All for me.
Don't mess about
Keep dishing them out
Interminably!

(HE SEARCHES DESK, PULLS OUT DRAWERS)

Where's that whatsit?
It's in the oojar,
I don't get it – why the fuss?
(ADDRESSING FILE) *Why not linger a little longer?*
Spend your life with us . . .
(PUTS IT BACK WHERE IT WAS)

ENTER MRS CHRISP TRUNDLING HER TEA TROLLEY.

The rest drowned by applause . . .